Test Items

SOCIOLOGY: HUMAN SOCIETY
SECOND EDITION

Melvin L. DeFleur
William V. D'Antonio
Lois B. DeFleur

Prepared by
Hugh F. Lena
Providence College

Scott, Foresman and Company   Glenview, Illinois
Dallas, Tex.   Oakland, N.J.   Palo Alto, Cal.   Tucker, Ga.   Brighton, England

ISBN: 0-673-97927

These Test Items for SOCIOLOGY: HUMAN SOCIETY, Second Edition, can
be used with both SOCIOLOGY: HUMAN SOCIETY, Second Edition, copyright
©1976, and SOCIOLOGY: HUMAN SOCIETY, Second Brief Edition, copyright
©1977. Users of the Brief Edition will be able to make use of the
materials for Chapters 1-12 and Chapter 20. Since the new Chapter 13
of the Brief Edition, on social institutions, contains material from
Chapters 15-19 of the regular edition, users of the Brief Edition can
select the appropriate material contained in Chapters 15-19 of these
Test Items.

1 2 3 4 5 6 7 8 -GBC- 80 79 78 77 76

INTRODUCTION

Preparing and administering student evaluations is a troublesome, although necessary, aspect of teaching. Examinations are a source of strain in the student-teacher relationship and may interfere with effective learning, but the prospects for alternative forms of evaluation within the present structure of American higher education are poor. Those who are teaching in a setting where only essay procedures need be used are lucky, but for most instructors, testing and grading with "objective" tests is an expected procedure. Time pressures, class sizes, and teaching loads often make such tests a practical necessity. Where this is the case, instructors have an obligation to prepare and use the best possible examinations they can construct.

Experts in test construction have developed their field into a complex specialty. Although sociologists have recently shown greater interest in teaching methods, as indicated by the introduction of graduate courses in teaching sociology and the advent of new professional journals on the subject, training in sociology seldom includes even the rudiments of test construction. Furthermore, experienced professors seldom pass on information regarding the effective construction and use of tests to new teachers. To fill this lack, these Test Items, along with suggestions for their use, have been provided.

Preparation of Items

Test Items for Sociology: Human Society, Second Edition, is a revised and updated version of Test Items, Set Number 1, prepared by Jo Ann Johnson and Melvin L. DeFleur. The revised set of Test Items borrows heavily from the previous set. Professors Johnson and DeFleur also prepared the section "Tips on Effective Testing," which has been retained with minor changes. Revised and updated textbook material--as much as 80 percent in some chapters--necessitated substantial reworking of some items and the addition of many new ones. Furthermore, many questions retained from Test Items, Set Number 1, have been reworded. These revisions more accurately reflect the content of the Second Edition of Sociology: Human Society, and they ensure that the items have not been widely circulated.

Considerable care was used in constructing Test Items for Sociology: Human Society, Second Edition. Some of the questions were selected by a panel of consultants from a variety of educational institutions to represent the concerns and viewpoints of educators who encounter a cross section of the American college population. Many of the items have been subjected to item analysis; questions with poor predictive capacity have been omitted from this booklet. It is hoped that the Test Items will be a useful guide for the construction and use of effective examinations.

Types of Items

A number of features characterize the present Test Items. The guiding principles in item construction have been thoroughness, diversity, and flexibility. These principles are reflected in consideration of the following categories of textbook material:

    a. major sociological concepts and their definitions;
    b. important hypotheses and theories under study;
    c. conclusions and generalizations from sociological research;
    d. application of sociological concepts and principles;
    e. sociological methods and techniques;

    f.   ideas of well-known sociologists;

    g.   debates and controversies.

Format

It is recognized that various instructors prefer different approaches to test construction and item format. For this reason, the format of Test Items makes use of various types of items, including multiple-choice, true-false, fill-in, matching, short essay, and broad essay questions. The short essays should require from a half to a whole page for most students, while the broad essays may require "blue books" or their equivalent. For each objective question in the Test Items, a preferred answer is indicated by an asterisk, based directly upon the manner in which the issue was discussed in the text. Page references are given for each item. For essay items, a list of noteworthy points is included beneath each item as suggested aids in grading.

Levels of Difficulty

In an attempt to allow instructors to select questions most appropriate for their classes, items fall within two major categories of difficulty. These are marked "LD" (less difficult) and "MD" (more difficult). The less difficult items are not "simpleminded"; they are based on the assumption that most classes are made up of individuals with varying levels of skill in reading and comprehending sociological ideas and material. These questions are often of the "recognition" type. That is, they give a definition of a given concept or theory and ask students to identify the correct term. The items marked "MD" are not "tricky," but do require a somewhat deeper grasp of sociological principles or concepts and an ability to apply them. Generally, the more difficult items ask students to select an illustration of a concept from a variety of examples.

Sampling of the Text

In selecting issues around which to construct items, an attempt has been made to develop questions from every major section of every chapter. This is most apparent with the multiple-choice questions, where at least one item in both the less and the more difficult categories has generally been included for each section. This was not possible for every type of item. Since fewer essay items are included, instructors may wish to construct additional ones.

Numbers of Items

For each chapter (with the exception of the shorter Epilogue) the following averaged numbers of items, formats, and levels of difficulty have been included. In some chapters the actual number of items will be slightly larger or smaller because of chapter length.

Levels of Difficulty	Multiple-Choice	True-False	Fill-In	Matching	Short Essay	Broad Essay
More Difficult	19	11	3	2	2	2
Less Difficult	19	11	3	2	2	2
Total:	38	22	6	4	4	4

Grand Total: 78

Tips on Effective Testing

The following is a brief summary of issues that instructors may wish to consider in developing, administering, and evaluating a given examination. No claim is made that all major considerations of effective testing are covered, but these are issues that occur with greater or lesser frequency in connection with testing at the college level in almost any subject matter. Instructors will undoubtedly have others to add.

Fairness

Perhaps no issue is more critical in the minds of students than whether their instructors are "fair" in the construction, administration, grading, and general use of tests. For the average student, a test's "fairness" translates into one that covers the material well and does not concentrate unduly on minor points and issues. It also translates into an orderly procedure for grading that the student understands, with adequate assurance of a reasonably high correlation between demonstrated performance and ultimate grade.

One minor technique worth considering is for the instructor to identify carefully the source of a given item or set of items in the test. For example, items drawn from the textbook can be prefixed by a "T" (text); those pertaining to material presented in lectures could be identified with "L"; those from supplemental readings might carry an "R" designation. This system of prefixing signals to the student that those sources of information, rather than personal experience or general knowledge, are to be drawn upon in answering the question. There are pros and cons regarding this procedure, but at least some students find it helpful, especially when varying views have been presented on a given issue or topic in the material to which they have been exposed.

More generally, instructors should give the greatest consideration to any feature of the testing program that will ensure that all students have a chance to achieve grades commensurate with their performance. Instructors should clearly understand their own criteria of fairness and be able to explain them to others.

Avoidance of Ambiguity

Students who lack an adequate grasp of the content of their course are often quick to charge that the test is composed of "ambiguous" items. In constructing the items in Test Items for Sociology: Human Society, Second Edition, the "preferred" answers are based solely upon the presentation of material in the textbook. If instructors have offered alternatives in class, or through additional readings, that give students conflicting sources from which to select an answer, the basis may have been laid for student feelings of confusion. Thus, not only the relatively unprepared student may see the item as ambiguous, but also the one who is very well prepared. It is essential, therefore, that the instructor review the information base from which every item in a test has been drawn. If there is any reason to believe that students will be confused in interpreting an item, then that item should not be included.

Sampling and Balance

An issue related to "fairness" and "lack of ambiguity" is that of sampling and balance. Selecting items for an examination is basically a sampling issue--but a sampling issue that must be tempered by an appropriate balance reflecting the presentation and coverage of the material by the instructor. A test will be seen as unfair if it unduly emphasizes lectures or concentrates too heavily on the text or ignores assigned readings. An excellent technique for preliminary test planning is to develop a weighting scheme before actual item selection or writing is undertaken. Thus the instructor might decide to devote, say, one third of the test points to material from the lectures, another third to textbook material, and another third to material from supplemental readings. Obviously, any other scheme would be appropriate, providing it reflects the balance of the course and has an underlying rationale. If no supplemental readings are used, the split might be fifty-fifty, and so on. In any case, the assignment of weight is made beforehand. Once this is done, the instructor can decide how many items of a given type can be included in that portion of the test and what number of points can be earned for each item.

Scheduling

Unless an instructor is committed to a philosophy of unannounced or "pop" quizzes, it is advisable to follow a procedure of scheduling tests well in advance. If students understand that the test will be given on a particular day, they can more adequately allocate their own time. Nothing is more exasperating to a student than to arrive ready to take the examination only to find that it has been postponed or rescheduled.

Grading

Students readily understand the principle of earning "100 percent" on an examination. Regardless of the number of items, item types, or weights given to specific items (such as a long essay), it is possible to transform any test to a scale of 100 percent. Thus, if a scheme has been developed whereby the total sum of points that can be earned in a given test is actually, say, 78, the total score that each student earns can be multiplied by 1.28 (100 divided by 78). Thus a student who earned all 78 points would receive a grade of 100 percent. One who got only half right would receive 50 percent (39 x 1.28), and so on. Course grades could then be based on averages or weighted averages of such test grades (avoiding the awkward business of trying to "average" letter grades).

There are literally thousands of ways in which instructors use test performance as a basis for motivating students to try to improve their performance. Some "drop" one test score; others make use of cutoff points or categories announced ahead of time. Thus, anyone who earns above a given cutoff point gets an "A" or a "B," etc., regardless of the "curve." The curve remains popular, particularly in those institutions that have an average student population. However, whatever may be the instructor's convictions and preferences in assigning grades on the basis of test performance or other criteria, the procedures should be definitely determined before instruction begins. There is no problem in modifying a plan if circumstances call for it, but to have no clear plan for evaluating tests and assigning grades until after the first test is given is to invite confusion on the part of both student and instructor.

Makeup Tests

Instructors vary greatly in the degree to which they are willing to permit students to make up tests that they have missed. It is a difficult business at best. The instructor is often forced into judging the validity of the student's excuse. It is also hard to make certain that the makeup test is as difficult (or easy) as the original. Thus those students who take the makeup test are either at an advantage or a disadvantage.

One possible solution to this dilemma is to prepare two examinations (at least in principle) at the time the original is constructed. The instructor, while going through the Test Items, can select items for the

regular test and at least mark the ones on which the makeup will be based.
This does not guarantee that the two forms will be identical in difficulty,
but with care they should be reasonably close. This requires some work,
but less than would be required later to construct a makeup exam that
parallels the original. In any case, a clear statement on makeup policies
will help students understand their situation and will help the instructor
with course planning.

Variety in Item Format

Some instructors feel strongly against items of a given type. They
may detest multiple-choice, or true-false, or some other form. There are
good and obvious reasons for preferring the more traditional and thorough
lengthy essay questions that give students ample opportunity to explore
the issues. But the sheer number of students and the pressures of time
often prevent the use of the more elaborate testing procedures. In any
event, if an objective type of test is to be used, care in item selection
can offset some of its shortcomings. For example, some students do poorly
at multiple-choice questions and handle matching questions better. Others
can handle true-false but not fill-in questions. Even with a large class,
it may be possible to use a "short essay" by providing a half page of
space for students to write out a succinct answer that can be graded
relatively quickly. Because of variations in students' skills, it may be
advisable to make use of several item formats in a given test, rather than
compose it of, say, only multiple-choice items. Few guidelines can be
laid down on this particular issue, but the major consideration should be
to develop a test that will let students demonstrate their command of the
material.

Correction for "Guessing"

An issue guaranteed to provoke heated discussion among educators is
that of correcting for guessing. Such a procedure consists of working out
the probability that a student can choose a given alternative correctly by
simple random processes. For example, the probability of guessing correctly
or incorrectly on a true-false item would be fifty-fifty. Thus a correction for guessing would be constructed by making the test score equal to the
number correct minus one half of the number wrong. In principle, this
would remove any benefit a student might get for guessing correctly. For
a multiple-choice item with five alternatives, the correction would be to
subtract one fifth of the number wrong. While such procedures are commonly
used in psychometric testing outside academic settings, they have not been
widely adopted by college instructors.

Item Analysis

Some instructors study the predictive capacity of the items included
in their tests by examining the extent to which a given item correlates
with the total score. Thus an item that is almost universally missed, or
one that is answered correctly regardless of whether the student is a high
or low overall performer, has little discriminatory power. It may be
advisable to eliminate such an item and recalculate the test scores before
returning the tests to the students. If this is done, the instructor will
have to establish different cutoff points. It helps to have IBM or similar
equipment and suitable computer programs available for handling item
analysis. Some institutions are prepared to handle such analyses routinely
for instructors.

Minimizing Cheating

Few of us like to admit that <u>our</u> students, for whom we have such high regard, would be capable of cheating. But if the pressures placed on students by parents and friends, anxiety about later goals, etc., are intense, a young person who is normally committed to "straight" values may be pushed into acts that constitute cheating. The best procedure for the instructor to follow is to arrange matters in such a way that cheating opportunities are minimized. In this way, students who would never cheat are protected, and those who might are protected from the pressures on them.

There are a variety of ways to minimize cheating temptations. One of the simplest is to use the <u>alternate forms</u> procedure of preparing the test. In this procedure, test items are not numbered on a given page. The pages are duplicated in the usual way, but the order of pages is reversed in every other test. Or, the pages can be mixed randomly. This provides alternative forms of a test with the same items. This simple mechanical procedure makes it slightly more difficult to grade the test with a key, but it is much more difficult for people in neighboring seats to figure out what alternative to select from their neighbors' papers. Another widely used system is to seat students in a large room (if available) with substantial space between each. Whatever system is used, most students will seldom resent such precautions. More often, those who have worked hard to prepare will feel protected by responsible security measures.

Returning and Discussing the Test

Instructors need to think through a plan for providing feedback for the students regarding the test. Many instructors prefer to retain the test themselves so that the items can be used on subsequent student populations. Others keep the tests so that the results will be available for consulting on grades. In either case the students can be given their papers in class and a discussion of the test can be provided, with the students making notes on points or issues that they need to review. The test papers can then be returned to the instructor. Other instructors may simply return the test for the students to keep. Whatever procedure is used, it is pedagogically sound to provide some form of review of the test material. It is at this point that instructors see the reward for sound test-construction procedures. If instructors have made every effort to ensure that the test is carefully graded, balanced, unambiguous, and appropriate in difficulty to the level of the class, it will be seen as effective and fair by the students. If not, student-faculty relationships will begin to deteriorate.

ACKNOWLEDGMENTS

The author would like to express his gratitude to Jo Ann Johnson and Melvin L. DeFleur, whose <u>Test Items, Set Number 1</u> provided the basis for this set of <u>Test Items</u>. For assistance in typing drafts of the <u>Test Items</u>, he would like to thank L. Norrine Smith, Jeannette Jackson, and Cheryl Guglielmi.

CONTENTS

CHAPTER 1.   The Science of Society

Multiple Choice

1.   (p. 3) (LD) One of the earliest systems of law used by a society to
     stabilize its social order was that of:
     a.   Auguste Comte;
     b.   Lester Ward;
     c.   Herbert Spencer;
    *d.   Hammurabi;
     e.   Thomas Hobbes.

2.   (p. 3) (MD) Ancient legal codes, such as Hammurabi's code, the laws
     of Manu, etc., represent:
     a.   the work of early research sociologists;
     b.   the beginnings from which modern sociology developed;
    *c.   systematic attempts to stabilize the social order and make it
          work more justly;
     d.   early examples of tyrannical political systems;
     e.   social reform movements at their very best.

3.   (p. 4) (LD) Many writers throughout history have attempted to produce
     reliable social knowledge. Until relatively recently, one of the main
     problems of such social theorists had been:
     a.   the lack of money to do adequate research;
    *b.   the lack of a reliable scientific method for verifying their
          conclusions;
     c.   a shortage of concepts and creative ideas concerning society;
     d.   opposition to their proposals from religious, military, or
          political leaders;
     e.   a general lack of enthusiasm for innovations on the part of rulers.

4.   (p. 5) (MD) Social theorists such as Comte and earlier social
     contract theorists shared the belief that:
     a.   the government has detrimental consequences for individuals;
    *b.   conflict should be eliminated, or at least minimized;
     c.   individuals do not have the right to overthrow the state;
     d.   conflict in society is essential and inevitable;
     e.   reform must take place through revolution.

5.   (p. 5) (LD) The view held by Hobbes, Locke, and Rousseau that people
     in the distant past had surrendered rights to an absolute government
     (sovereign) in order to protect individuals from one another and to
     achieve an orderly society is usually called:
     a.   the induction theory;
     b.   the age of reason;
    *c.   the social contract theory;
     d.   the political deduction theory;
     e.   the hedonistic theory.

6.   (p. 5) (LD) The name sociology was given to the new science of
     society by:
     a.   Karl Marx;
     b.   Herbert Spencer;
     c.   Henri de Saint-Simon;

*d. Auguste Comte;
 e. Jean Jacques Rousseau.

7. (p. 6) (MD) Auguste Comte formulated one of the early descriptions
    of the "organic" nature of society, based upon its structure, func-
    tional interdependence of parts, and pattern of evolution from a
    simple to a more complex form. He classified society as a:
    *a. collective organism;
     b. biological system;
     c. socio-biological complex;
     d. cultural conjunction;
     e. rational organization.

8. (p. 7) (MD) The relationship between social problems and govern-
    mental action advocated by Herbert Spencer could best be described as:
     a. rational activism;
     b. natural selection;
    *c. laissez faire;
     d. organic functionalism;
     e. universal evolution.

9. (p. 7) (LD) Social Darwinism was advocated mainly by:
     a. Charles Cooley;
    *b. Herbert Spencer;
     c. Auguste Comte;
     d. Karl Marx;
     e. Henri Saint-Simon.

10. (p. 7) (LD) Both Karl Marx and Herbert Spencer formulated theories
     of:
      a. the communistic society;
      b. Social Darwinism;
      c. the class system;
     *d. the nature of social change;
      e. the overthrow of capitalism.

11. (p. 8) (MD) By collecting and analyzing suicide statistics in
     European countries over a period of years, Durkheim was able to
     conclude that:
      a. poor people and those at the very top of society are the most
          likely to commit suicide;
      b. suicide is especially unlikely during periods of financial crises,
          such as depressions;
     *c. integration into cohesive groups (e.g., family) influences the
          individual's likelihood of various types of suicide;
      d. social scientists could predict that an individual would commit
          suicide;
      e. the suicide rate is a product of urbanization and degree of
          industrialization.

12. (p. 10) (LD) According to Durkheim, the term anomie describes:
      a. a kind of suicide caused by excessive loyalty to one's group or
          society;
      b. the reason why suicide rates are high among Catholics;
      c. a form of suicide among persons weakly integrated into a
          cohesive group;

*d. a condition of a society (or group) in which confusion and
    contradiction exist concerning social norms;
 e. the basic trend in social organization in European nations.

13. (p. 10) (MD) Durkheim's 1897 monograph on <u>Suicide</u> was of special
     significance to early sociology because it showed that:
     a. biology had no place in explaining human social conduct;
    *b. sociology could make a unique contribution to understanding a
         social problem;
     c. psychological explanations of deviant behavior were completely
         inadequate;
     d. human behavior could be adequately explained by cultural factors
         alone;
     e. suicide was on the rise all over Europe and was becoming a major
         problem.

14. (p. 10) (LD) European sociology in the nineteenth century was mainly
     concerned with:
     a. developing a science of societal phenomena for its own sake;
     b. understanding human social behavior for economic purposes;
    *c. achieving social reform by systematically studying society;
     d. manipulating people for political purposes--that is, controlling
         public opinion;
     e. finding solutions to political instability and reducing the rate
         of social change.

15. (p. 10) (LD) Sociology first became established in the United States:
    *a. during the final decades of the nineteenth century;
     b. shortly after the beginning of World War I;
     c. about the time of the Great Depression of the 1930s;
     d. about the time of the American Civil War;
     e. early in the nineteenth century, about ten years later than in
         Europe.

16. (p. 10) (LD) One of the major reasons the new discipline of sociology
     was attractive in the American setting was:
     a. the disenchantment of Americans with government attempts to
         achieve social reform;
     b. the failure of leaders in education and organized religion to
         solve social problems;
    *c. the existence of numerous social displacements and severe social
         problems in the United States at that time;
     d. the willingness of American political leaders of the time to
         accept uncritically almost anything of European origin;
     e. the heritage of slavery, which demanded a new science to help
         achieve racial integration.

17. (p. 10) (LD) Early sociologists in the United States concentrated
     their attention mainly upon:
     a. political issues;
     b. problems of race relations;
     c. developing an abstract science;
    *d. the study of social problems;
     e. integrating sociology and statistics.

18. (p. 11) (MD) The study of contemporary sociology, as broadly defined in the text, focuses on:
  *a. the organizational properties of societies, their patterns of change, and their problems;
  b. the social ills produced by the economic processes of society;
  c. the way in which governmental systems influence other forms of social behavior;
  d. limited areas of social behavior--that is, criminology, race relations, and the family--insofar as these cause social problems;
  e. the way in which people conform to basic social rules and achieve stable societies.

19. (pp. 15-17) (LD) Which of the following is not an issue in contemporary sociology?
  a. Verstehen versus neopositivistic approaches to behavior;
  b. social equilibrium versus social conflict;
  *c. systematic versus unsystematic study of society;
  d. social science versus social amelioration;
  e. all of the above are issues.

20. (p. 21) (MD) Many sociologists today think of their field as a basic science. This means that sociology:
  *a. seeks to validate with factual evidence hypotheses and theories of human social life that may or may not have practical applications;
  b. is more significant than such applied sciences as psychology and anthropology;
  c. tries to find the basis for correcting deviant behavior;
  d. focuses mainly on such basic problems as alcoholism, divorce, and crime;
  e. tends to be more precise than economics or history.

21. (p. 21) (MD) A "symbol" that labels, in an agreed-upon relationship, a particular situation, object, or event of nature that a scientist has under study is usually referred to as a:
  *a. concept;
  b. generalization;
  c. construct;
  d. term;
  e. datum.

22. (p. 21) (MD) Concepts whose properties vary are often called:
  a. complexes;
  b. constructs;
  *c. variables;
  d. data;
  e. hypotheses.

23. (p. 22) (LD) Statements or propositions describing a relationship between two or more concepts are usually called:
  *a. generalizations;
  b. concepts;
  c. variables;
  d. complexes;
  e. meanings.

24.   (p. 23) (MD) A hypothesis may be defined as:
       a.   a generalization confirmed by empirical evidence;
     *b.   a generalization unconfirmed by empirical evidence;
       c.   an extremely precise concept;
       d.   an unacceptable theory;
       e.   a scientific fact or datum.

25.   (p. 22) (MD) A statement relating two or more concepts in such a way
       that it also summarizes factual evidence concerning the relationship
       is called:
       a.   an observational summary;
       b.   a tested conclusion;
       c.   a verified theory;
     *d.   an empirical generalization;
       e.   a conclusive hypothesis.

26.   (p. 23) (MD) Valid theories are of great importance to sociologists
       because:
       a.   they summarize the opinions of many sociologists;
       b.   they provide invariant laws that constitute scientific truths;
       c.   they provide speculative guesses of the reasons for human social
            conduct;
       d.   they show people how to behave to lead more moral lives;
     *e.   they provide comprehensive explanations of social phenomena.

27.   (p. 24) (LD) The term science (in the sense of the scientific method)
       can best be thought of as:
       a.   a set of precise measurement techniques that scientists use in
            their work;
       b.   the procedures used in such fields as physics and chemistry for
            doing precise work;
       c.   the experimental method, whether in the physical, biological,
            or social sciences;
     *d.   a set of rules for ensuring that research will lead to valid
            generalizations and theories;
       e.   a method for convincing people of the validity of one's
            speculations.

28.   (p. 26) (LD) In an experimental research design, the factor which
       the researcher systematically changes or varies to study its effect
       on other factors is called:
       a.   the dependent variable;
     *b.   the independent variable;
       c.   the interaction variable;
       d.   the controlled variable;
       e.   none of the above.

29.   (p. 28) (LD) Propositions in social science are generally stated as:
       a.   absolutes;
     *b.   probabilities;
       c.   closed entities;
       d.   being subject to qualification;
       e.   b and c only.

30.   (p. 28) (LD) Sociological predictions, based upon theory and
       research:

a. are normally valid for a period of only about ten years;
b. are seldom wrong because they are usually concerned with rather obvious events;
c. have continuing problems because they are made on the basis of conflicting opinions;
d. show what each individual will do in a given category of persons;
*e. seldom attempt to predict what specific persons will do, but assign probabilities of given behavior to categories of people.

31. (p. 28) (MD) The discussion of the death penalty in Michigan, Ohio, and Indiana showed that:
a. the death penalty definitely served as a deterrent to homicide in the three states;
b. all three states showed a drop in homicide rates after adopting the death penalty;
*c. the existence or nonexistence of the death penalty in a given state did not influence the homicide rate of that state;
d. none of the states could lower their homicide rates effectively with a death penalty;
e. in each state homicide rates rose after the death penalty was adopted.

32. (p. 27) (MD) The Tools of Sociology on "Interpreting Statistical Tables" stressed that:
a. one must always suspect that tables contain numerous errors;
b. few tables really say much about reality because human life cannot easily be reduced to numbers;
c. tables of statistical data are fundamental to sociological activism;
d. such statistical information is always objective or neutral;
*e. careful study of the title, sources, labels, and units of a table is a key to understanding what it presents.

True-False

33. (p. 2) (LD) The primary concern of contemporary sociologists is the solution of social problems.
a. true;
*b. false.

34. (pp. 3-4) (LD) The major obstacle for early social theorists was the lack of a reliable method for empirically testing their hypotheses.
*a. true;
b. false.

35. (p. 2) (LD) Ancient codes like Hammurabi's laws and legal codes today are similar in that they are based upon the traditional customs of a society.
*a. true;
b. false.

36. (p. 4) (LD) In his quest for a perfect society, Plato described a utopian Greek city-state in which justice was maximized.
a. true;
*b. false.

37. (p. 5) (MD) Thomas Hobbes was a social and political philosopher who argued that without a strong political authority, people would behave toward each other as beasts.
   *a. true;
   b. false.

38. (p. 6) (MD) Comte theorized that societies go through three stages of development, and he advocated that in the third stage the governance of a society should be the responsibility of sociologists.
   *a. true;
   b. false.

39. (p. 6) (MD) For Comte, as for many other early theorists, social conflict is an inevitable part of the social process.
   a. true;
   *b. false.

40. (p. 7) (MD) According to Herbert Spencer, carefully executed legislation by the government would result in more adequate solutions for social problems.
   a. true;
   *b. false.

41 (p. 7) (LD) Herbert Spencer believed that the natural evolution of society would ultimately lead to social progress.
   *a. true;
   b. false.

42. (pp. 7-8) (MD) Herbert Spencer and Karl Marx both viewed social conflict as an intrinsic (very basic) part of human life.
   a. true;
   *b. false.

43. (pp. 7-8) (LD) According to Marx, social progress could best be achieved by active intervention (revolution) of certain social classes (proletariat).
   *a. true;
   b. false.

44. (p. 8) (MD) One important characteristic of the pioneers of modern sociology--those of the late nineteenth century (e.g., Durkheim and Weber)--was their orientation toward the study of society as it was, rather than as it ought to be.
   *a. true;
   b. false.

45. (p. 10) (MD) As sociology established itself in the United States toward the end of the nineteenth century, it concentrated almost exclusively on accumulating knowledge and becoming a basic science of society.
   a. true;
   *b. false.

46. (p. 10) (MD) In the United States sociology was equated with "social reform" partly because of the increasing number of social problems created by urbanization and industrialization.

*a. true;
b. false.

47. (p. 14) (LD) Sociology differs from other social sciences in that it concentrates on human interaction in general rather than on one particular area of social life.
*a. true;
b. false.

48. (p. 17) (LD) Value judgments almost always enter into sociologists' consideration of social conflict.
*a. true;
b. false.

49. (p. 22) (LD) A generalization, in scientific usage, is a statement about the relationship between two or more hypotheses.
a. true;
*b. false.

50. (p. 28) (MD) Sociology bases the majority of its theories and generalizations upon controlled observations under experimental conditions.
a. true;
*b. false.

Fill-In

51. (p. 4) (MD) The one major problem faced by early social theorists was the lack of a _____ _____.

scientific method

52. (p. 6) (LD) The idea that society should be led by a "priesthood" who understood positivistic sociology was advocated by _____ _____.

Auguste Comte

53. (p. 5) (MD) _____ _____ was credited with giving the name "sociology" to the "science of society" and establishing it as a discipline.

Auguste Comte

54. (p. 8) (LD) Revolution is to Marx as _____ is to Spencer.

evolution

55. (p. 8) (LD) The monograph on suicide by _____ _____ contributed much to the development of early research techniques and new areas in which sociology could be used.

Émile Durkheim

56. (p. 23) (MD) The central importance in developing theories is that they provide _____ of social phenomena.

explanations

Matching

57. (pp. 4-6, 22-23) (MD)
     absolute government   theories
     social physics   Plato
     explanation   Thomas Hobbes
     hypotheses   Auguste Comte
     ideal society   generalizations

58. (pp. 4-7, 22-23) (MD)
     Francis Bacon   generalizations
     quantitative   evolution
     explanation   deduction
     René Descartes   theories
     Herbert Spencer   induction

59. (pp. 5-8) (LD)
     Herbert Spencer   early American sociology
     social reform   the name "sociology"
     Thomas Hobbes   proletariat and bourgeoisie
     Auguste Comte   Social Darwinism
     Karl Marx   social contract

60. (pp. 5-8) (LD)
     Das Kapital   Durkheim
     positivism   Plato
     suicide   Auguste Comte
     perfect society   Herbert Spencer
     Social Darwinism   Karl Marx

61. (pp. 21-23) (LD)
     summary of factual evidence   concept
     set of interrelated generalizations   variable
     miniature system of meaning   empirical generalization
     concept whose properties come in   generalization
         differing amounts
     meaningful relationship between   theory
         two or more concepts

62. (p. 9) (MD)
     anomic suicide   low rate among Catholics
     egoistic suicide   rate increases during war
     altruistic suicide   distinctively related to
                                                suicide
     social involvement   unrelated to suicide
     extra-social factors   duty to take one's life

Short Essay

63. (p. 6) (MD) Many early social theorists wrote about the "organic
     nature of society." For example, Auguste Comte described society as
     a "collective organism." In general, what characteristics of society
     led such writers to this kind of conceptualization?

     Major points: society has structure; its parts function inter-
     dependently; it evolves from simple to complex.

64. (p. 6) (LD) Name some of the principal ideas of Auguste Comte.

Major points: positivism; organic theory of society; law of three stages.

65. (pp. 8-14) (MD) In its formative years, what were the principal areas of study in the discipline of sociology?

Major points: broad organization properties of society; nature and processes of social change; the problem aspects of society.

66. (pp. 21-22) (LD) Distinguish the terms (a) concept, and (b) generalization.

Major points: a concept is a label (symbol) for that which it stands (phenomenon); a generalization is a statement of relationship between two or more concepts.

67. (p. 22) (MD) What is meant by an empirical generalization?

Major points: a statement of meaningful relationship between two or more concepts that also summarizes factual evidence concerning the relationship.

68. (p. 23) (LD) Why are theories important for sociologists?

Major points: they provide explanations of social phenomena; they suggest lines of further inquiry.

Broad Essay

69. (pp. 3-4) (LD) Name and summarize briefly the ideas of two individuals who were important in the prescientific origins of sociology.

Major points: answer will vary according to persons chosen; these could be Hammurabi, Plato, Bacon, Descartes, Hobbes, Locke, or Rousseau.

70. (pp. 7-8) (MD) Discuss the difference between the theories of social change advanced by Karl Marx and Herbert Spencer.

Major points: Spencer: evolution, natural selection, no planned change; Marx: political revolution, economic determinism--people and means of production.

71 (p. 9) (MD) Discuss the conceptual scheme and the research strategy employed by Durkheim in his famous study of suicide.

Major points: he hypothesized that there were several distinctive patterns of suicide (egoistic, anomic, and altruistic), each brought about by distinctive patterns of integration into groups; he assembled official records on suicide from various countries in order to compare different categories of people who were integrated into a variety of groups.

72. (pp. 10-11) (LD) Discuss the principal reasons why sociology found a relatively ready acceptance in the United States after its initial development in Europe.

Major points: it was oriented toward social problems, which were

numerous in the U.S.; the colleges of the U.S. often lacked inhib-
iting academic traditions; the new field promised to find solutions
through the scientific study of society.

73. (pp. 15-17) (MD) Identify three issues in contemporary sociology and
discuss the merits of opposing perspectives on these issues.

Major points: the subjective orientation of the Verstehen approach
versus the objective techniques of the neopositivistic approach to
the study of human behavior; social equilibrium versus social conflict orientations to social behavior; the pursuit of scientific
knowledge versus seeking solutions to social problems.

74. (pp. 24-28) (LD) Outline the steps that constitute the "scientific
method" and briefly explain each.

Major points: formulation of research questions (stating testable
hypotheses) and research designs; gathering data through controlled
observation (with dependent and independent variables identified);
analyzing results, often with use of statistical techniques; and then
reaching generalizations that describe, predict, or explain behavior.

75. (pp. 27-28) (LD) How could one study sociologically whether severe
penalties for possession of marijuana reduce the rate of marijuana use
in a state?

Major points: this parallels the death-penalty example on p. 28;
investigator could select states that have similar cultural characteristics but that vary in punitiveness regarding marijuana; public
records regarding such arrests could be analyzed and compared;
probable conclusion: severity of penalty is unrelated to rate of
behavior.

76. (p. 27) (MD) What were the principal points made in the essay on
"Interpreting Statistical Tables"?

Major points: special attention should be paid to the following:
title, source, column and row labels, units or rates, and combinations of characteristics.

CHAPTER 2. Social Organization

Multiple Choice

77. (pp. 32-33) (LD) Games such as football and baseball share which of
the following organizational properties with other human groups?
   a. a system for ranking members differentially;
   b. mutually understood patterns of interaction that shape the
       behavior of members;
   c. a framework of general rules that members are expected to follow;
   d. individually and collectively valued goals;
  *e. all of the above.

78. (p. 33) (MD) According to the text, a human group is:
  *a. a number of individuals who interact recurrently according to

some pattern of social organization;
b. a number of persons who know each other and feel a sense of belonging;
c. two or more people who share a common way of life--that is, a common culture;
d. a number of people who share a common characteristic such as a given income level, amount of education, etc.;
e. a number of individuals who recurrently come into close physical proximity with each other.

79. (p. 33) (LD) The term used to describe a number of individuals who share some common characteristic, or cluster of characteristics, but who lack the components of social organization is:
   a. social group;
   b. informal group;
  *c. social category;
   d. formal conglomerate;
   e. subcultural aggregate.

80. (p. 34) (MD) An important feature that distinguishes a group from a social category is:
   a. group guides;
  *b. group norms;
   c. opinion outlooks;
   d. informal understandings;
   e. formal prescriptions.

81. (p. 34) (MD) Social interaction that is nonrecurrent and relatively unstructured can be called:
   a. collective;
   b. informal;
   c. unpredictable;
  *d. transitory;
   e. unstable.

82. (p. 35) (MD) When group members generally understand the rules for interpersonal behavior and expectations of each other but do not attempt to specify such rules and expectations in clear or written terms, resulting interaction is likely to be:
   a. unpredictable;
  *b. informal;
   c. random;
   d. illegal;
   e. deviant.

83. (p. 35) (LD) Which of the following would be characterized by the least amount of formal social interaction?
   a. the Navy;
   b. the factory;
  *c. the peer group;
   d. the Audubon Club;
   e. the Salvation Army.

84. (p. 35) (LD) Interaction proceeding on the basis of clearly speci-fied (usually written) rules can be called:

a. informal;
b. legal;
c. official;
*d. formal;
e. structured.

85. (p. 36) (MD) The stabilizing process which serves to maintain the norms of a group by providing standard ways for coping with needs and achieving group goals is called:
*a. institutionalization;
b. social policy;
c. group formation;
d. normative integration;
e. embedding of customs.

86. (p. 36) (LD) The process of developing orderly, stable, and increasingly predictable forms of recurrent interaction is called:
a. standardization;
*b. institutionalization;
c. embedding;
d. stabilizing;
e. traditionalizing.

87. (p. 37) (MD) A social group must have:
a. a formal goal;
*b. members who behave in somewhat predictable ways;
c. transitory interaction;
d. a manifest goal;
e. a leader who directs behavior of the membership.

88. (pp. 37-39) (LD) Norms are:
a. regularities of behavior;
b. expected patterns of behavior;
c. supported by group consensus;
d. b and c only;
*e. a, b, and c.

89. (p. 38) (LD) Shared convictions about patterns of behavior that are appropriate or inappropriate for the members of a group are referred to as:
a. group guides;
*b. group norms;
c. opinion outlooks;
d. informal understandings;
e. formal prescriptions.

90. (pp. 38-39) (MD) An important distinction between formal and informal norms lies in the fact that:
a. formal norms provide guides to group conduct while informal norms do not;
b. formal norms must be obeyed but informal norms only suggest lines of action;
*c. informal norms emerge without conscious planning while formal norms are usually deliberately designed;
d. informal norms are institutionalized while formal norms are not;

e. formal norms require individual compliance while informal norms pertain mainly to social categories.

91. (p. 39) (MD) Norms clearly reduce individual freedom, but they make life less complicated because:
    a. everyone wants to be told what to do;
    b. no one wants unlimited freedom--it is against human nature;
    c. norms are always simpler than other shared prescriptions for action;
    *d. norms make social relationships more predictable;
    e. norms are much better than laws, which would be necessary in the absence of norms.

92. (p. 40) (LD) The development of a division of labor in a group, based upon specialized expectations for different members, is called:
    a. task assignment;
    b. function division;
    *c. role allocation;
    d. role placement;
    e. work assignment.

93. (p. 40) (MD) Social roles develop in a group out of which of the following necessities?
    a. the division of labor;
    b. the collective accomplishment of certain goals;
    c. the innate human need to specialize;
    d. all of the above;
    *e. only a and b.

94. (p. 40) (MD) The development of specialized expectations for different members of a group is called:
    a. normative confusion;
    b. division of labor;
    c. ascription;
    *d. role allocation;
    e. goal development.

95. (p. 40) (LD) Which of the following is not an ascribed criterion used by groups to allocate roles?
    a. age;
    b. sex;
    *c. education;
    d. race;
    e. all of the above are ascribed criteria.

96. (p. 40) (LD) Criteria for social ranking based upon factors about which the individual can do little or nothing are called:
    a. proscribed;
    b. prescribed;
    *c. ascribed;
    d. inscribed;
    e. achieved.

97. (pp. 40-41) (MD) Leadership in groups and societies arises directly out of which of the following necessities?

a. role allocation;
*b. role coordination;
c. role conflict;
d. role expectation;
e. role reciprocation.

98. (p. 41) (LD) If a large gap develops between role expectations and role behavior, which of the following would be predicted?
*a. conflict;
b. banishment;
c. integration;
d. tolerance;
e. reinforcement.

99. (p. 42) (LD) Almost all groups permit minor deviations from normative expectations. That is, most norms have some sort of:
a. deviation boundary;
b. eccentricity value;
c. violation coefficient;
d. normative component;
*e. tolerance limits.

100. (pp. 41-42) (MD) <u>Sanctions</u> are:
a. negative, interpersonal acts intended to bring transgressors into line;
*b. rewards or punishments for deviation from or conformity to group expectations;
c. positive reinforcements that make people support group norms;
d. behaviors which are approved within a group;
e. techniques for reducing the gap between role expectations and role behaviors.

101. (p. 42) (MD) Tolerance limits are seldom:
a. present in groups;
b. related to deviance from role definitions;
*c. precisely defined;
d. vaguely defined;
e. related to deviance from norms.

102. (p. 43) (LD) According to the text, the level of prestige accorded to group members because they play a particular role in a group can be called:
a. class;
*b. status;
c. rank;
d. position;
e. place.

103. (p. 43) (MD) The text uses the term <u>status</u> to mean:
a. amount of wealth of a given family;
*b. level of prestige associated with a role;
c. social ascription of achieved criteria;
d. role position in a social structure;
e. power in a ranked hierarchy.

104. (p. 47) (MD) The distinction between ascribed and achieved criteria for social ranking is that:
    a. the individual can usually do nothing about the achieved criteria but can do something about ascribed criteria;
    b. the individual can always improve ascribed criteria but seldom improve achieved criteria;
    *c. the individual can usually do something about achieved criteria but not about ascribed criteria;
    d. ascribed criteria pertain to the ranking of younger people while achieved criteria are applicable to older people;
    e. ascribed criteria pertain mainly to females and achieved criteria mainly to males.

105. (p. 48) (LD) Sociologists who stress stability and equilibrium as normal conditions of group life are likely to take which of the following perspectives?
    *a. social systems perspective;
    b. a Verstehen orientation;
    c. stability hypothesis;
    d. conflict perspective;
    e. antidisturbance perspective.

106. (p. 49) (LD) William Foote Whyte's classic Street-Corner Society provides an excellent example of the methodology of:
    a. statistical inference;
    b. controlled experiments;
    *c. participant observation;
    d. transitory interaction;
    e. formal structure.

107. (p. 46) (MD) The sociogram is an example of the use of which of the following research approaches?
    a. the Verstehen approach;
    *b. the neopositivistic approach;
    c. the psychological approach;
    d. the subjective approach;
    e. the Marxist approach.

108. (p. 50) (LD) In a social system, unanticipated and unrecognized consequences are called:
    a. manifest functions;
    b. unwitting functions;
    *c. latent functions;
    d. unplanned functions;
    e. latent manifestations.

109. (p. 50) (MD) In a functional analysis of a social system, the term function refers to:
    *a. the contribution a given component makes to the system's stability;
    b. the way in which a group really operates internally and externally;
    c. the manner in which roles are related to norms;
    d. the interrelationship between social sanctions and role performance;

   e. the degree to which the group's actual behavior differs from
       ideal behavior.

110. (p. 50) (LD) The contribution of a given component in a social
      system to the equilibrium of that system would be called that
      component's:
      a. effect;
      b. outcome;
      c. equilibrium coefficient;
     *d. function;
      e. dysfunction.

111. (p. 50) (LD) A given practice in a group that hampers the achieve-
      ment of group goals or disrupts a group's equilibrium would be
      termed:
     *a. dysfunctional;
      b. disequilibrium;
      c. antistabilizing;
      d. latent;
      e. manifest.

112. (p. 50) (LD) Student strikes and demonstrations in colleges and
      universities in recent years have sometimes disrupted their opera-
      tions. From the point of view of administrators, such events would
      be regarded (within a social systems perspective) as:
      a. antiestablishment;
      b. latent functions;
      c. manifest disruptions;
      d. nonfunctional;
     *e. dysfunctional.

113. (p. 54) (LD) During the Chicago convention riots in 1968, as dis-
      cussed in the text, the police were brought in to maintain order.
      However, many individual policemen desired to punish the demonstra-
      tors. Such a situation can be described sociologically as an
      example of:
      a. inadequate supervision;
     *b. goal conflict;
      c. poor training;
      d. transitory interaction;
      e. police corruption.

114. (p. 54) (MD) One of the key elements in preventing the disintegra-
      tion or breakdown of a group as a cohesive social system is the
      maintenance of:
      a. a regular application of negative sanctions;
      b. a fixed ranking structure;
      c. clear-cut latent goals;
     *d. established channels of communication;
      e. a broad division of labor.

115. (p. 55) (MD) During the Chicago convention riots of 1968, the rules
      of conduct that normally maintain police discipline became confused
      and ineffective. Émile Durkheim might have characterized such a
      situation as an example of:

a. disintegration;
b. disorganization;
*c. anomie;
d. dysfunction;
e. dyscohesion.

116. (p. 55) (LD) A group in which the rules of conduct are so weakened or confused that they no longer provide effective behavioral guides (as, for example, when the Chicago police force tried to control the convention riots of 1968) is characterized by:
a. cultural inconsistency;
*b. normative confusion;
c. ineffective consensus;
d. disharmonious functions;
e. dysfunctional attitudes.

117. (p. 56) (MD) Differing expectations of the manner in which a person will carry out activities in a group (e.g., expectations for scholar vs. teacher on the part of a college professor) can be called:
*a. internal role conflicts;
b. external role conflicts;
c. dysfunctional role anomie;
d. role confusion effects;
e. cultural lag.

118. (pp. 55-57) (LD) Marty, an academically serious college student, is asked by his friend to help him cheat on an exam. Sociologically, this would be an example of:
*a. role conflict;
b. anomie;
c. normative integration;
d. communicative breakdown;
e. social disequilibrium.

119. (pp. 56-57) (MD) Members of the Chicago police force who were involved in the convention disturbances of 1968 had reason to doubt that they would be punished for violating the department's official rules of conduct when handling the riot. Such a situation can be characterized sociologically as:
*a. ineffectiveness of social control;
b. disturbances in latent functions;
c. dysfunctional group goals;
d. external role conflicts;
e. normative restriction.

120. (p. 58) (MD) During the Chicago convention riots of 1968, the demonstrators taunted the police with cries of "fascist pigs" and various obscenities. The police, on the other hand, referred to dissenting citizens as "hooligans," "un-American," and "radicals." Such names imply:
a. unfair symbolization;
b. immoral attitudes;
c. ineffectiveness of social sanctions;
*d. disturbances in social ranking;
e. intergroup role conflicts.

121. (p. 58) (LD) According to the text, social conflict and social
tension:
a. must be eliminated from groups;
b. are universally negative in their consequences;
*c. are normal parts of group life;
d. never have positive consequences;
e. always have positive consequences.

122. (p. 60) (MD) Positive functions of social conflict were discussed
in the textbook. These did not include:
a. the clarification of issues;
b. increased group integration;
*c. the elimination of conflict-prone people;
d. the stimulation of change;
e. the provision of external targets for group hostilities.

True-False

123. (p. 34) (LD) A social category is defined as a number of people who
share a common characteristic.
*a. true;
b. false.

124. (p. 34) (MD) Social categories can be a factor in the development
and structuring of organized groups in that group members are often
drawn from specific categories.
*a. true;
b. false.

125. (pp. 34-35) (MD) Transitory interaction differs from recurrent
interaction primarily in the degree of intensity of the interactions.
a. true;
*b. false.

126. (p. 35) (LD) Informal interaction differs from formal interaction
in that it does not follow any rules.
a. true;
*b. false.

127. (p. 35) (MD) Both informal and formal interaction patterns have
their own set of norms which arise in such a way that conflict
between them seldom occurs.
a. true;
*b. false.

128. (p. 36) (MD) Institutionalization is the process of developing
orderly, stable, and increasingly predictable forms of recurrent
interaction.
*a. true;
b. false.

129. (p. 36) (LD) One of the conditions necessary for the formation of a
group is coordinated interaction to attain specific goals.
*a. true;
b. false.

130. (p. 36) (LD) Unlike formal groups, informal groups do not have to
     mesh the individual goals of their members.
      a. true;
     *b. false.

131. (p. 39) (LD) Conformity to a particular norm depends on its contri-
     bution to group goals.
     *a. true;
      b. false.

132. (p. 40) (LD) In every group, the expectations and activities rele-
     vant to each role are clearly unrelated to those of other roles.
      a. true;
     *b. false.

133. (p. 40) (LD) Ascribed criteria are often a consequence of much
     training or schooling.
      a. true;
     *b. false.

134. (p. 43) (LD) Individuals who belong to different groups with con-
     flicting norms may risk the negative sanctions of one group for the
     positive sanctions of the group with which they more strongly identify.
     *a. true;
      b. false.

135. (p. 48) (MD) Systems theorists believe that groups tend toward
     stability and equilibrium and that they show unyielding resistance
     to change.
      a. true;
     *b. false.

136. (p. 50) (LD) Something is dysfunctional if it somehow hampers a
     group from attaining its goals.
     *a. true;
      b. false.

137. (p. 50) (MD) The term dysfunctional has meaning only from a given
     perspective of interests or values.
     *a. true;
      b. false.

138. (pp. 50, 54) (LD) Conflict between the manifest and latent goals of
     the police was definitely not one focal point of trouble during the
     Chicago riots.
      a. true;
     *b. false.

139. (p. 58) (MD) One likely consequence of the intrusion of emotional
     and psychological needs of individuals into formal relations is the
     breakdown of the system of social ranking.
     *a. true;
      b. false.

140. (p. 60) (LD) Conflict may help people to become aware of issues
     that have been hidden or overlooked.

*a.   true;
 b.   false.

141.   (p. 60) (MD)   Conflict may induce change but usually at the cost of
       a group's dissolution.
        a.   true;
       *b.   false.

Fill-In

142.   (p. 36) (MD)   The process of developing orderly, stable, and increas-
       ingly predictable forms of recurrent interaction is called

       _____.

       institutionalization

143.   (p. 36) (LD)   When the members of a group have clearly specified
       their goals and understand them explicitly and completely, then these
       goals may be said to be _____.

       manifest

144.   (p. 40) (MD)   A group's development of a division of labor based
       upon assigning specialized expectations to different members is
       called _____ _____.

       role allocation

145.   (p. 43) (MD)   _____ is derived from a role and designates
       the level of prestige given an individual.

       Status

146.   (p. 44) (MD)   The concept of _____ defines a configuration
       of parts that are in a dynamic relationship of interdependency.

       system

147.   (p. 50) (LD)   If some practice is said to be _____ in a
       social system, it means that it somehow hinders the attainment of
       group goals.

       dysfunctional

148.   (p. 46) (LD)   A _____ is a chart graphically presenting the
       results of a sociometric analysis.

       sociogram

Matching

149.   (pp. 34-36, 49) (LD)
       participant observation   basis of group organization
       formal interaction   research technique
       informal interaction   relatively unstructured
       transitory interaction   clearly specified rules
       meaningful communication   loosely formulated rules

150. (pp. 37-39) (MD)
     universal norm   being a "tattletale"
     formal norm   monogamy in United States
     norm configuration   a leader
     specialized norm   a legal statute
     informal norm   wearing lipstick

151. (pp. 38-41, 49) (LD)
     participant observation   role coordination
     universal norms   supported by group consensus
     development of leadership   folkways and mores
     division of labor   Verstehen approach
     effective norms   role allocation

152. (pp. 38-46) (LD)
     sociogram   role allocation
     formal norms   clique, star, isolate
     division of labor   role coordination
     status   rationally designed rules
     leadership   prestige of a role

153 (pp. 40-47) (MD)
     achieved criteria   personal quality
     ascribed criteria   consequence of role prestige
     esteem   age, sex
     status   exceeding group requirements
     positive sanctions   occupation, education

154. (pp. 48-51) (MD)
     ineffectiveness of social control   equilibrium assumption
     dysfunction   unrecognized consequence
     functional analysis   meaningless sanctions
     latent function   organic perspective
     social system   hampers group goals

Short Essay

155. (pp. 34-35) (LD) Discuss the difference between transitory and
     recurrent interaction.

     Major points: transitory--relatively unstructured and nonrecurrent;
     not shaped by social organization with norms, roles, and sanctions;
     recurrent--shaped by social organization with goal-oriented inter-
     action.

156. (p. 40) (MD) Briefly explain why the allocation of roles is an
     important element in a group's social organization.

     Major points: allows for the development of a division of labor
     with specialization and coordination of activities which helps to
     organize the behavior and expectations of the group; this helps the
     group to attain its goals more effectively.

157. (p. 40) (LD) Sociologists make a distinction between achieved and
     ascribed criteria. Discuss the difference briefly.

     Major points: ascribed criteria--the individual cannot do anything about them; achieved criteria--the individual can do something about them.

158. (p. 40) (MD) Discuss some of the characteristics of latent functions.

Major points: unintentional; unrecognized; unanticipated consequences.

159. (pp. 51-58) (LD) Discuss one of the sociological factors that were sources of conflict within the Chicago police department during the 1968 Democratic Convention.

Major points: answer may be one of the following: conflict in group goals, breakdown in communication, normative confusion, role conflict, ineffectiveness of social control.

160. (p. 60) (MD) Discuss one positive consequence of social conflict.

Major points: answer may be one of the following: clarification of issues, group integration, stimulation of change.

Broad Essay

161. (p. 37) (LD) Name and explain briefly the principal components of social organization.

Major points: norms are patterns of expectation that groups establish; roles are configurations of specialized rights, duties, and obligations allocated to particular group members; social control techniques ensure that members will follow norms and roles; and ranking systems are developed that accord group members different levels of prestige, power, and privilege.

162. (p. 37) (MD) Belonging to a group with a pattern of social organization reduces the freedom of individuals in that it imposes a system of expectations and controls over their behavior. What are the components of such groups and what advantages do they hold for the individual members?

Major points: components are: norms, roles, social control, and ranking system; advantages are: increasing predictability of social relationships and thus ease of interaction.

163. (p. 47) (LD) What are the basic principles concerning the equilibrium of social systems (groups)?

Major points: groups have a tendency to maintain themselves and resist disturbance from the outside; stability and equilibrium are relative; groups adapt to changing circumstances; this change is gradual and does not disrupt basic structure.

164. (pp. 51-58) (LD) The text describes the way in which the components of social organization were involved in the breakdown of police discipline during the Chicago convention riots of 1968. Explain and give examples.

Major points: answer should include explanation of: normative confusion (anomie), role conflict, ineffectiveness of social control, and disturbances in social ranking.

165. (p. 55) (LD) Émile Durkheim developed the concept of anomie. How can such an idea help us understand an event such as the Chicago convention riots of 1968?

Major points: each side had different conceptions of their rights (norms); norms pronounced by Mayor Daley conflicted with official police regulations; public opinion held still other norms concerning police action needed to preserve law and order; such normative confusion was an important factor in reducing clarity of what action the interacting parties should take.

166. (p. 46) (MD) The data obtained from sociometric analysis is often represented in a sociogram. Name and explain some of the principal patterns that can emerge from such a procedure.

Major points: mutually attracted pair, star, power behind the throne, isolate, nonreciprocated chain, clique.

CHAPTER 3. Types of Groups

Multiple Choice

167. (p. 63) (LD) Which of the following distinctions is the basis of feelings of ethnocentrism that many groups develop?
   a. primary versus secondary;
   b. membership versus reference;
   *c. in-group versus out-group;
   d. formal versus informal;
   e. manifest versus latent.

168. (p. 64) (MD) Among the following, which group would probably not be classified as a primary group?
   *a. a small group of friendly people who have recently met on a ship;
   b. a clique of close friends in school;
   c. a rural family who moves to a city;
   d. a large urban family whose members live in different neighborhoods;
   e. a group of close friends at work.

169. (p. 65) (LD) Primary groups can be distinguished from other small groups in that:
   *a. their patterns of social organization are different;
   b. only blood relatives are members;
   c. they are larger;
   d. the members are younger;
   e. the members are related by birth or marriage.

170. (p. 66) (LD) One of the most important conditions for developing and maintaining open channels of communication characteristic of primary groups is:
   *a. physical nearness;
   b. spatial separation;

c. good verbal facility;
d. high social skills;
e. an open mind on most issues.

171. (p. 66) (MD) Which of the following is not characteristic of primary group interaction and communication?
a. high level of self-disclosure;
b. physical nearness is essential for developing and maintaining open channels of communication;
c. members respond to each other in terms of complete personalities;
*d. members rarely get to know each other intimately;
e. all of the above are characteristic of primary groups.

172. (p. 66) (LD) An important basis of group solidarity in a primary group is:
*a. a shared feeling of common identity;
b. a clear-cut division of labor;
c. formally defined role expectations;
d. specialization of role assignments;
e. a strong interlinking of specialized functions.

173. (p. 67) (LD) Interaction in the primary group tends to:
*a. reduce social distance;
b. enhance rank distinctions;
c. emphasize social stratification;
d. reshape social ranks in reverse;
e. do any or all of the above.

174. (p. 67) (MD) Which of the following statements correctly describes the social control practices of primary groups?
a. self-generated controls are important;
b. self-administered sanctions are used;
c. informal sanctions predominate;
d. both positive and negative sanctions are used;
*e. all of the above.

175. (p. 68) (LD) From a sociological point of view, such groups as committees, commissions, councils, juries, and boards of supervisors can be viewed as:
*a. formal decision-making groups;
b. informal secondary groups;
c. formal primary groups;
d. artificial decision-making groups;
e. informal primary groups.

176. (p. 68) (MD) Such bodies as committees, commissions, councils, juries, boards, etc., can be classified as formal decision-making groups because:
*a. of their distinct patterns of social organization;
b. decisions are made by their members;
c. they have formal norms and goals;
d. their formal goals are principally related to decision-making;
e. they have small numbers of decision-making members.

177. (p. 68) (MD) Research by Bales and Strodtbeck indicates that inter-action in formal decision-making groups seems to develop in stages.

Which of the following is <u>not</u> such a stage?
a. collecting information;
b. evaluating information;
c. reaching a decision;
d. restoring an equilibrium;
*e. institutionalizing sanctions.

178. (p. 70) (MD) Weber proposed which of the following criteria for the construction of "ideal types"?
a. they must generate hypotheses;
b. they must be contrived;
c. they must accentuate reality;
*d. all of the above;
e. none of the above.

179. (p. 70) (LD) Max Weber developed an analytical method based upon accentuated "mental constructs" that are abstracted from observations of societal phenomena. He called these:
*a. ideal types;
b. pure types;
c. constructed types;
d. model types;
e. polar types.

180. (p. 69) (LD) Studies of social ranking within formal decision-making groups confirm the principle that:
*a. the status and roles individuals have outside the group help determine the positions they enjoy within the group;
b. the status of people in such a group depends upon their personal warmth and appeal;
c. physical appearance is the main basis for status within such groups;
d. such groups seldom have a clear-cut system of ranking because members are equal;
e. the status of all persons in such a group is derived from their occupations.

181. (p. 71) (MD) Among the following, which are major principles underlying bureaucratic organization?
*a. rationality and efficiency;
b. impersonality and informality;
c. efficiency and simplicity;
d. complexity and inefficiency;
e. informality and complexity.

182. (p. 71) (LD) Within large, formally organized groups, the prevailing pattern of social organization is:
*a. bureaucratic;
b. democratic;
c. informal;
d. manifest;
e. latent.

183. (p. 72) (LD) From a sociological point of view, the official norms of a school system can be classified as:

*a. formal;
 b. latent;
 c. informal;
 d. democratic;
 e. inflexible.

184. (p. 74) (MD) In most associations, social control is based upon:
 *a. voluntary submission to authority;
 b. mutual emotional satisfaction;
 c. the application of strong negative sanctions;
 d. constant use of positive sanctions;
 e. selected application of force.

185. (p. 74) (MD) The key concept in understanding social control in the association is:
 *a. contract;
 b. ideal type;
 c. bureaucracy;
 d. sanction;
 e. loyalty.

186. (p. 74) (MD) The theory of bureaucratic organization specifies that the system of social ranking is based upon:
 *a. competence;
 b. nepotism;
 c. income;
 d. favoritism;
 e. status.

187. (p. 74) (MD) Within the association, the middle-level administrators are sometimes referred to sociologically as:
 *a. functionaries;
 b. foremen;
 c. junior executives;
 d. manipulators;
 e. coordinators.

188. (p. 75) (LD) Unofficial practices and procedures that arise and become institutionalized within associations are referred to as:
 *a. informal structure;
 b. spontaneous organization;
 c. unofficial norms;
 d. latent role systems;
 e. bureaucratic organization.

189. (pp. 75-77) (MD) Which of the following could not be a consequence of informal structure in an association?
 a. it impedes goal achievement;
 b. it injects new goals into the group;
 c. it contributes to goal achievement;
 d. it redefines lines of communication;
 *e. all of the above are consequences.

190. (p. 80) (LD) The primary goals of the community are basically:
 *a. economic;
 b. emotional;

c. esthetic;
d. defensive;
e. informal.

191. (p. 80) (MD) Community attention to such issues as the arts, educa-
      tion, and civic beautification are viewed sociologically as examples
      of:
   *a. secondary goals;
    b. esthetic orientations;
    c. significant objectives;
    d. dysfunctional pursuits;
    e. organizational purposes.

192. (p. 81) (MD) Role structures in small communities (as compared to
      larger cities) tend to be more:
   *a. integrated;
    b. isolated;
    c. alienated;
    d. differentiated;
    e. associated.

193. (p. 83) (MD) At the community level, social ranking as a character-
      istic of social organization is usually a pattern of:
   *a. stratification;
    b. exploitation;
    c. institutionalization;
    d. formalization;
    e. communication.

194. (p. 83) (MD) In Western societies, most communities arrange their
      families into a:
   *a. class system;
    b. associational pattern;
    c. bureaucratic structure;
    d. anonymous system;
    e. aggregate pattern.

195. (p. 84) (LD) A type of social relationship based upon reciprocal
      and binding sentiments, mutual trust, and willing cooperation can be
      called:
   *a. Gemeinschaft;
    b. bureaucracy;
    c. association;
    d. Gesellschaft;
    e. communality.

196. (p. 86) (LD) In the Gesellschaft, the principal instrument for
      defining the obligations of interaction is the:
   *a. contract;
    b. informal agreement;
    c. traditional obligation;
    d. mutual expectation;
    e. reciprocal sentiment.

197. (p. 86) (MD) Among the following, which would most likely be charac-
      terized by a Gemeinschaft type of social relationship?

*a.   a rural village;
 b.   a labor union;
 c.   a committee;
 d.   a large city;
 e.   the U.S. Navy.

198.   (p. 88) (LD) Widespread norms that are chance-like in origin and
       established as common practices for numerous routine areas of
       behavior are referred to by sociologists as:
       *a.   folkways;
        b.   mores;
        c.   rituals;
        d.   social practices;
        e.   routine norms.

199.   (p. 88) (MD) Which of the following would best illustrate a viola-
       tion of the mores in American society?
       *a.   an incestual relationship;
        b.   wearing unusual clothing;
        c.   failing to go to church;
        d.   buying liquor after legal hours;
        e.   public drunkenness.

200.   (p. 91) (LD) At the societal level, most social control is actually
       achieved by:
       *a.   voluntary submission to rules;
        b.   vigorous application of negative sanctions;
        c.   the use of force on a selective basis;
        d.   the use of positive sanctions;
        e.   rational application of the folkways and the mores.

201.   (p. 92) (MD) Which basic social institution would Marxian theory
       stress in accounting for the process of societal change?
       *a.   economic;
        b.   educational;
        c.   political;
        d.   familial;
        e.   religious.

202.   (p. 92) (LD) Broadly organized patterns of goal-oriented activities
       that have become deeply institutionalized in a society can be re-
       ferred to as:
       *a.   social institutions;
        b.   complex communities;
        c.   clusters of folkways;
        d.   interlinked mores;
        e.   voluntary associations.

203.   (p. 76) (MD) Peter Blau's study Dynamics of Bureaucracy was based
       upon which of the following methods?
        a.   participant observation;
        b.   use of statistical records;
        c.   interviews;
       *d.   all of the above;
        e.   none of the above.

True-False

204. (p. 65) (MD) A group is characterized as a primary group to the extent that it emphasizes interaction as an end in itself.
     *a. true;
      b. false.

205. (p. 67) (LD) An important consequence of primary interaction is the increase of social distance between people.
      a. true;
     *b. false.

206. (p. 68) (LD) Formal decision-making groups may often be arenas for power struggles and competitive maneuvering.
     *a. true;
      b. false.

207. (p. 69) (MD) Sociologists have found little relationship between the status one has outside a decision-making group and the status one has within the group.
      a. true;
     *b. false.

208. (p. 71) (LD) Bureaucracy is the prevailing pattern of formal social organization in associations.
     *a. true;
      b. false.

209. (p. 74) (MD) In a bureaucratic structure such as an association, authority tends to be vested in the role rather than in the individual.
     *a. true;
      b. false.

210. (pp. 77-78) (MD) In his study of bureaucratic organizations, Peter Blau found impersonality to be an important condition for maintaining organizational effectiveness.
      a. true;
     *b. false.

211. (p. 79) (LD) A community differs from most other groups in that it has a distinct spatial location.
     *a. true;
      b. false.

212. (p. 80) (LD) The primary goals of communities have always been basically political.
      a. true;
     *b. false.

213. (p. 80) (LD) Primary interaction is more likely to exist among residents of a metropolis than among small-town residents.
      a. true;
     *b. false.

214. (p. 81) (MD) Roles tend to be less closely integrated in a large community than in a smaller one.
*a. true;
 b. false.

215. (p. 81) (MD) The greater diversity of people in urban communities, as compared with small towns, requires a greater reliance upon formal norms to regulate conduct.
*a. true;
 b. false.

216. (p. 83) (LD) Usually members of a community are ranked as families.
*a. true;
 b. false.

217. (p. 84) (LD) In most Western industrial societies, stratification systems are based primarily on ascribed criteria.
 a. true;
*b. false.

218. (p. 84) (LD) A societal goal is meaningful and operative only if it expresses the shared values of a majority of the society's members.
*a. true;
 b. false.

219. (p. 84) (MD) The trend from status to contract refers to the shift from family relationships to those in which persons could act independently in entering into binding interactions with others.
*a. true;
 b. false.

220. (p. 86) (MD) The term Gemeinschaft implies a relationship built upon individualism while Gesellschaft implies a relationship based upon sentiment.
 a. true;
*b. false.

221. (p. 88) (LD) Folkways are associated with intense feelings of right and wrong.
 a. true;
*b. false.

222. (p. 89) (MD) Legal statutes that are not rooted in the informal norms of a society are often unenforceable.
*a. true;
 b. false.

223. (pp. 90-91) (MD) In his study of the division of labor in both traditional and industrial societies, Durkheim concluded that an extended division of labor (characteristic of urban societies) increased the differences among people, thus eliminating the basis for social solidarity.
 a. true;
*b. false.

Fill-In

224. (p. 65) (LD) A _____ group is maintained more for its own sake than for accomplishing specified goals.

primary

225. (p. 71) (LD) Bureaucracy is the prevailing pattern of social organization in _____.

associations

226. (p. 71) (MD) The underlying principles of bureaucratic organization are _____ and _____.

rationality and efficiency

227. (p. 84) (MD) In modern industrial societies, social stratification systems are usually based upon _____ criteria.

achieved

228. (p. 86) (LD) Tönnies hypothesized two "ideal types" of social relationships. In his scheme, urbanization would lead to an increase in the _____ relationship.

Gesellschaft

229. (p. 86) (MD) Tönnies hypothesized that the _____ relationship is one of mutual trust, concern, and willing cooperation for common goals.

Gemeinschaft

230. (p. 88) (LD) _____ cover and regulate behaviors that are associated with intense feelings of right and wrong.

Mores

231. (p. 90) (MD) The type of social cohesion based upon common sentiments (as advanced by Durkheim) is called _____ solidarity.

mechanical

Matching

232. (p. 63) (MD)
consciousness of kind   in-group
reference group   source of opinions
secondary group   impersonal
out-group   no sense of identity
primary group   "we" feeling

233. (pp. 63-64) (LD)
primary group   source of emotional
                                       satisfaction
secondary group   relatively impersonal
decision-making group   stages of interaction
peer group   similarity of age and interests
reference group   opinions important

234. (pp. 79-83) (LD)
      community's primary goals   economic
      community's secondary goals   art, education, esthetics
      community's spatial arrangement   ecological pattern
      community as group   distinctive organization
      community's functions   integrative social system

235. (pp. 84-87) (MD)

      Gemeinschaft   reciprocal sentiment
      Gesellschaft   contract
      associative   Gesellschaft
      communal   Gemeinschaft
      mass society   superficial relationships

236. (pp. 87-89) (LD)
      violations of mores   intense feelings of right and
                                             wrong
      nature of folkways   institutionalized expectation
                                             for routine matter
      origin of laws   formalization of code of
                                             conduct
      effective laws   support in mores
      violation of folkways   low intensity of feelings

237. (pp. 90-91) (MD)
      limited division of labor   results in interpersonal
                                             similarities
      cohesion based on specialization   organic solidarity
      cohesion based on likeness   mechanical solidarity
      extended division of labor   results in individual differ-
                                             ences
      division of labor in society   determines type of solidarity

Short Essay

238. (pp. 65-66) (LD) Describe the type of interaction that is charac-
      teristic of a primary group.

      Main points: based upon open communication; involves proximity;
      responses in terms of complete personalities; consequences of inter-
      action are interpersonal enjoyment and reduction of social distance.

239. (pp. 75-78) (LD) Why is the development of an informal structure
      within an organization important?

      Main points: formal structure may not get the job done, so individ-
      uals may follow unofficial procedures; may inject new and unofficial
      goals into the group; may supplement or subvert official techniques
      of social control.

240. (p. 80) (MD) Discuss the distinction made in the text between
      primary and secondary goals of a community.

      Main points: primary goals are economic and are related to growth
      and decline of communities; secondary goals are not important in

maintaining the community but rather meet the needs of people to interact.

241. (pp. 84-87) (MD) The movement of industrial societies toward impersonal forms of interaction has been discussed by many sociologists. Ferdinand Tönnies discussed this trend by hypothesizing two types of social relationships, Gemeinschaft and Gesellschaft. Briefly define both.

Main points: Gemeinschaft: binding relationship based upon sentiment; it is a relationship of mutual trust; Gesellschaft: characterized by individualism, contractual obligation, and mutual distrust; relationship is basically competitive.

242. (pp. 87-88) (LD) Two types of societal norms are folkways and mores. Compare the two types.

Main points: folkways: institutionalized expectations about social conduct; low intensity of feeling associated with them; mores: intense feelings of right and wrong; they regulate more critical forms of behavior.

243. (pp. 90-91) (MD) In Durkheim's analysis of the social significance of the division of labor, what was his reasoning in assuming that industrial societies also maintain group stability and solidarity?

Main points: extended division of labor results in much specialization and although this specialization tends to separate members of the society it also makes them mutually dependent while making various groups interdependent.

Broad Essay

244. (pp. 65-67) (LD) Describe the characteristics of primary groups as patterns of social organization.

Main points: goals: often an end in themselves; interaction: open communication, face-to-face response to whole person; norms: strong, informal, unique; roles: limited division of labor, informal; social control: informal, self-generated and administered; ranking: tends to minimize social distance.

245. (pp. 65-67) (MD) Select a primary group from your own experience and analyze its organizational characteristics from a sociological orientation.

Main points: answer will vary in specifics but should focus on goals, interaction, norms, roles, control, and ranking.

246. (pp. 68-69) (LD) Analyze the organizational patterns of typical small decision-making groups.

Main points: goals: manifest and formal plus latent and informal; interaction: proceeds by stages; norms: prescribed formal procedures; roles: formal and informal; social control: informal and formal; ranking: outside roles and status influence in-group ranking.

247. (pp. 71-75) (LD) Outline and discuss the major features of bureaucratic organization as these are described in formal organizational
theory.

Main points: based upon rationality and efficiency, formal goals,
channeled interaction, official norms, fixed roles, control by consent and contract, and ranking based on competence.

248. (pp. 79-80) (MD) In what sense is a community an "integrative"
social system?

Main points: It is composed of numerous sub-groups; these interact
as component parts of the system; the community is the overall structure that regulates this complex of interacting persons and sub-
groups.

249. (pp. 84-87) (LD) Discuss the meaning of Tönnies' concepts Gemeinschaft and Gesellschaft.

Main points: these are "ideal types" of social relationships em-
bodying the following characteristics: Gemeinschaft--intimate,
mutual binding sentiment, reciprocal trust, welds people into a
common unity; Gesellschaft--individualism and distrust; contract
important for defining interactional obligations; these are abstract
constructs; not descriptions of a real society.

250. (pp. 92-94) (MD) What are "social institutions" and which institutions are most universal?

Main points: a cluster of institutionalized practices pertaining to
a broad goal-oriented area of human life (including groups, beliefs,
attitudes, etc.); all societies have political, economic, educational,
familial, and religious institutions.

251. (p. 70) (MD) Discuss the use of "ideal types" as a procedure in
sociological analysis. Show how ideal types were used by sociological pioneers.

Main points: answer should be based upon Weber's three criteria
(accentuate reality, contrived model, generate hypotheses); examples
could be drawn from Weber (bureaucracy), Durkheim (types of suicide),
Comte (Law of Three Stages), Tönnies (Gemeinschaft and Gesellschaft),
etc.

CHAPTER 4. Culture and Subculture

Multiple Choice

252. (p. 96) (LD) Sociologists define culture as:
    a. appreciation of literature and the fine arts;
    b. people's accumulated solutions to recurring problems;
    c. the social heritage of a given society;
    d. a people's total pattern of beliefs, customs, institutions,
        objects, and techniques;
  *e. all above but a.

253. (p. 94) (LD) Two important steps in the development of material culture were related to:
  a. the invention of the sail and the spear;
  b. the development of weapons and the wheel;
  *c. the use of tools and the mastery of food gathering;
  d. hunting and gathering techniques;
  e. the use of fire and the manufacturing of clothing.

254. (p. 97) (MD) The basic condition for the development of culture among human beings, which is present in much lesser degrees among lower animals, is:
  a. the ability to respond to a spiritual being;
  b. a sense of moral responsibility;
  c. the ability to imitate others;
  d. a stronger biological constitution;
  *e. an enormous learning capacity.

255. (p. 98) (MD) An important precondition to the development of both social organization and culture is the ability to use:
  a. agriculture;
  b. tools;
  c. fire;
  d. the wheel;
  *e. symbols.

256. (p. 99) (MD) Insects such as termites, bees, and ants:
  *a. lead an organized life but do not develop culture;
  b. have elements of both social organization and culture in their life;
  c. lead a life characterized by a rigid culture;
  d. lead a life characterized by only a narrow culture with clear specialization;
  e. have a clear division of labor and a narrowly defined culture.

257. (p. 100) (LD) Among the following, which are important comparative characteristics of culture?
  a. cultural solutions to problems are variable;
  b. cultures tend toward internal consistency;
  c. cultural standards are relative;
  d. only a and c above;
  *e. all of the above (a,b,c).

258. (p. 100) (MD) The studies of ethnographers are important in understanding human cultures because they make possible:
  a. moral perspectives;
  *b. cross-cultural comparisons;
  c. elaborate official records;
  d. psychiatric therapy;
  e. ethnographic observations.

259. (p. 100) (LD) Anthropologists who make descriptive studies of the cultural patterns of societies are called:
  a. demographers;
  *b. ethnographers;
  c. culturographers;

d. sociographers;
e. variographers.

260. (p. 102) (MD) Available evidence indicates that the native or genetic learning capacity of today's bright city child, as compared with those of a bright child of an upper Paleolithic family, is:
a. substantially greater;
b. only a little greater;
*c. about the same;
d. clearly inferior;
e. impossible to determine.

261. (p. 102) (LD) An important determinant of cultural differences between peoples is:
a. environment;
b. available materials;
c. amount of contact with others;
d. cultural heritage of the past;
*e. all of the above.

262. (p. 102) (LD) The fact that societies around the world vary greatly in their standards of beauty, logic, truth, morality, etc., is called by social scientists cultural:
a. variability;
*b. relativity;
c. differentiation;
d. heterogeneity;
e. unlikeness.

263. (p. 103) (MD) A nation regards its own foods as vastly more tasty and "civilized" than those of any other society. This would be an example of:
*a. ethnocentrism;
b. cultural relativity;
c. gourmet sensitivity;
d. group superiority;
e. good cultural taste.

264. (p. 103) (LD) Sociologists use which of the following terms to describe the tendency of groups to regard their own ways as superior and to look down on the ways of others?
a. in-group perspective;
b. group superiority;
c. snobbery;
d. cultural relativity;
*e. ethnocentrism.

265. (p. 104) (LD) A culture in which there are no significant contradictions between people's beliefs and their actions or between one set of beliefs and another is said to be:
a. incongruous;
b. amalgamated;
*c. consistent;
d. assimilated;
e. equilibrated.

266. (p. 107) (LD) American culture is more likely than Zuñi culture to
be characterized by:
*a. conflict and competition;
b. harmony and consistency;
c. morality and honor;
d. sensibility and insight;
e. stupidity and ugliness.

267. (p. 107) (LD) Viewed as a whole, Zuñi culture can be said to be
quite:
a. warlike;
b. dysfunctional;
c. primitive;
*d. integrated;
e. competitive.

268. (p. 105) (MD) According to Ruth Benedict, the "ideal man" in Zuñi
is:
*a. noncompetitive with dignity and affability;
b. of a crafty and competitive nature;
c. a person who knows how to beat others at all games;
d. of great physical strength;
e. high in aptitude as a hunter.

269. (p. 107) (MD) In contrast to Zuñi culture, American culture can be
said to be:
a. morally unacceptable;
b. rotten to the core;
*c. divisive and disharmonious;
d. based on false promises;
e. vastly superior.

270. (p. 109) (MD) Which of the following best illustrates the analytic
approach to the study of culture?
a. a social scientist relates a number of cultural units into a configuration;
b. an anthropologist describes the folktales of a primitive society;
c. a sociologist analyzes the census records of France;
*d. a social scientist attempts to identify the smallest meaningful
units in a given hunting procedure;
e. any of the above.

271. (p. 109) (LD) The smallest meaningful units of cultural content are
called cultural:
a. units;
*b. traits;
c. bits;
d. elements;
e. solutions.

272. (p. 109) (MD) Which of the following provides an example of a cultural trait?
*a. the bow and arrow taken together;
b. the arrow;
c. the bowstring;

d.　the wooden part of the bow;
e.　any of the above.

273.　(p. 109) (LD)　The approach to the study of culture that seeks to
identify, describe, and classify individual units of culture is
called the:
a.　synthetic approach;
*b.　analytic approach;
c.　unit approach;
d.　quantitative approach;
e.　logistic approach.

274.　(p. 109) (LD)　The approach to the study of culture that seeks to
identify, describe, and explain broad cultural patterns is called the:
*a.　synthetic approach;
b.　analytic approach;
c.　pattern approach;
d.　qualitative approach;
e.　logistic approach.

275.　(p. 109) (LD)　All the physical objects that people in a society
make (weapons, clothing, tools, etc.) are collectively called:
a.　fabricated traits;
b.　art forms;
c.　cultural traits;
*d.　material culture;
e.　technical artifacts.

276.　(p. 110) (MD)　The basic sentiments and emotionally held orientations
of approval-disapproval held by members of a society are called:
*a.　evaluative culture;
b.　symbolic culture;
c.　belief culture;
d.　judgmental culture;
e.　moral culture.

277.　(p. 110) (MD)　During the Middle Ages, Europeans commonly believed
the world to be flat. This belief is part of the category of culture
called:
a.　incorrect postulates;
b.　cosmic beliefs;
*c.　symbolic traits;
d.　regulative traits;
e.　none of the above.

278.　(p. 111) (LD)　The attitudes toward virginity and virility in Brazil
are examples of:
*a.　normative traits;
b.　cultural complexes;
c.　sexual permissiveness;
d.　cultural relativity;
e.　all of the above.

279.　(p. 112) (LD)　A set of guiding beliefs that make the people of a
given society distinctive and unique is called its:

a. informal structure;
b. culture complex;
c. subculture;
*d. ethos;
e. configuration.

280. (p. 112) (LD) A pattern of norms, beliefs, attitudes, and values shared by particular groups or segments of a society, but which does not characterize the society as a whole, is called:
a. an ethnic group;
b. a social institution;
*c. a subculture;
d. a folkway;
e. the informal structure.

281. (p. 112) (MD) Among the following, which would be most likely to have developed a subculture?
a. people over 21 years of age;
b. commuters to a city center;
c. tourists who visit Florida;
*d. inmates in a prison;
e. individuals with brown hair.

282. (pp. 113-118) (MD) According to the textbook, which of the following is a distinctive characteristic of the carnival?
a. it is a deviant subculture;
b. it integrates its members into the rest of society;
c. it is dying out rapidly;
*d. it has organization and a stratification system;
e. none of the above.

283. (pp. 113-118) (MD) Which of the following does not apply to the carnival?
a. it has a subculture;
b. it has its own argot and cant;
c. it has a specialized technology and distinctive values;
*d. it is not part of the American cultural heritage;
e. all of the above apply to the carnival.

284. (pp. 118-120) (MD) Which one of the following groups would not develop a subculture?
a. the medical profession;
b. marijuana smokers;
c. Native Americans (American Indians);
d. New Englanders;
*e. all of the above might develop subcultures.

True-False

285. (p. 96) (LD) In reference to any particular group of people, most social scientists accept the validity of using the contrast "cultured versus uncultured."
a. true;
*b. false.

286. (p. 96) (MD) Culture is created and maintained by its society and
     is therefore dependent upon individual members for existence.
     a. true;
     *b. false.

287. (p. 96) (LD) One of the more interesting facts about human cultures
     is the tendency to choose very similar ways of meeting the universal
     human needs for food, clothing, and shelter.
     a. true;
     *b. false.

288. (p. 97) (LD) Two early steps in the development and evolution of
     material culture were the discovery of techniques for farming and
     the acquisition of social organization.
     a. true;
     *b. false.

289. (p. 99) (LD) The difference between culture and social organization
     lies in whether or not a group or society has an accumulated social
     heritage that each new individual must learn.
     *a. true;
     b. false.

290. (p. 100) (MD) Social organization establishes the limits for cultural
     development.
     a. true;
     *b. false.

291. (p. 102) (LD) The great variability in ways that people have solved
     problems of food, shelter, etc., is caused by variations in native
     learning capacity.
     a. true;
     *b. false.

292. (p. 102) (MD) Aldous Huxley touched upon some of the important
     variables contributing to cultural differences. These variables
     were kind of environment, materials available, contact with other
     societies, and kind of value orientations.
     a. true;
     *b. false.

293. (p. 103) (MD) Ethnocentrism is felt to be predominantly dysfunc-
     tional for a group or society.
     a. true;
     *b. false.

294. (p. 104) (LD) A fully integrated culture is one in which there are
     no significant contradictions between people's beliefs and their
     actions, or between one set of actions or beliefs and another.
     *a. true;
     b. false.

295. (p. 107) (MD) One reason the American culture is less consistent
     than the Zuñi culture is because our values do not come from a
     single cultural heritage.

*a. true;
 b. false.

296. (p. 109) (LD) The analytic approach to the study of culture seeks
      to discover broad cultural patterns within a society.
       a. true;
      *b. false.

297. (p. 110) (MD) The term <u>cultural complex</u> refers to any cluster of
      related traits around which people organize their lives, <u>except</u> for
      the material objects such as tools, etc.
       a. true;
      *b. false.

298. (p. 110) (LD) A cultural complex is a cluster of related traits
      around which people organize some aspect of their lives.
      *a. true;
       b. false.

299. (p. 112) (MD) Urban and industrialized societies are characterized
      by many subcultures, the vast majority of which are not supported by
      society as a whole.
       a. true;
      *b. false.

300. (p. 112) (MD) The Puritan ethic remains as a basic value orienta-
      tion in most Western cultures.
      *a. true;
       b. false.

301. (p. 113) (LD) Unlike more general cultures, subcultures have content
      but they do not have structure.
       a. true;
      *b. false.

302. (p. 118) (MD) A given subculture may be shared by numerous specific
      groups.
      *a. true;
       b. false.

303. (p. 119) (MD) Religious subcultures frequently develop out of a
      common national origin.
      *a. true;
       b. false.

304. (p. 120) (LD) In a society such as ours, few individuals belong to
      subcultures.
       a. true;
      *b. false.

Fill-In

305. (p. 99) (MD) _____ gives direction to and sets limits on
      patterns of social organization to be developed within a society.
      Culture

306. (p. 102) (LD) Because of cultural variability, judgments of the merits of given solutions must be made on a basis of cultural

_____.

relativity

307. (p. 103) (MD) _____ may be a source of conflict between groups and a source of unity within groups.

Ethnocentrism

308. (p. 104) (LD) When a culture is internally consistent in its pattern of values, beliefs, and behavior, then it is said to be _____.

integrated

309. (p. 109) (LD) The _____ approach to the study of culture seeks to identify, describe, and classify culture traits.

analytic

310. (p. 112) (MD) The _____ of a society is a synthesis of the guiding beliefs that give the people of that society a distinctive makeup.

ethos

311. (p. 112) (LD) Extensive social differentiation found in urban and industrialized societies is a source of the numerous _____ which characterize such societies.

subcultures

Matching

312. (pp. 96-99) (LD)

termites	no culture
social heritage	culture
culture	solutions to problems
basis of communication	symbols
necessary condition for cultural development	enormous learning capacity

313. (pp. 97-100) (MD)

culture and society	distinct
social heritage and culture	similar
social insects	lack culture
uneducated people	have culture
basis of culture	learning capacity

314. (pp. 100-105) (LD)

ethnography	descriptive anthropology
cultural differences	not due to intellectual capacity
all human societies	same average of native intelligence
slowly changing	Zuñi culture

315. (pp. 100-104) (LD)
cultural relativity
cultural variability
ethnocentrism
cultural integration
universally accepted standards

contrasting moral codes
diversity of solutions
feeling of group superiority
few contradictions
nonexistent

316. (pp. 102-104) (MD)
extreme ethnocentrism
societal sex standards
differing standards of
    logic, beauty, etc.
promotes in-group solidarity
universal moral standard
    accepted by all human cultures

self-destructive
vary greatly
cultural relativity

mild ethnocentrism
nonexistent

317. (pp. 105-109) (MD)
Zuñi culture
American culture
integrated culture
noncompetitive
diverse origins

consistent
internal conflicts
few contradictions
ideal "Zuñi man"
American culture

318. (pp. 113-118) (LD)
in-group
"mark"
cooling the mark out
manner of speech
specialized vocabulary

consciousness-of-kind
customer
"patch"
cant
argot

Short Essay

319. (p. 100) (MD) Briefly explain the distinction between culture and society.

Major points: society: large number of individuals engaged in recurrent interaction and in maintaining a distinctive pattern of social organization; culture: specific system of beliefs, objects, practices, etc., passed from one generation to another.

320. (pp. 103-104) (MD) What is "ethnocentrism" and how is it important?

Major points: ethnocentrism: tendency of a group to regard its own ways as superior and to look down on the ways of all others; it is both a source of conflict between groups and a source of unity and stability within groups.

321. (p. 104) (LD) Describe the difference between a culture that is integrated and one that is not.

Major points: culturally integrated: no significant contradictions between beliefs and actions or between one set of actions or beliefs and another; internally consistent in their patterns of values, beliefs, and behavior.

322. (pp. 112-113) (LD) What are subcultures and what are some of the bases for their development?

Major points: subculture: a pattern of norms, beliefs, attitudes, values, and other elements that are shared within particular segments of a society but that don't normally characterize the society as a whole; occupations, religion, social class, age group, etc., may be bases for development of subcultures.

Broad Essay

323. (p. 96) (LD) What do sociologists mean by the term <u>culture</u>?

Major points: total pattern of beliefs, customs, institutions, objects, and techniques of a people; social heritage, accumulated solutions to problems; distinct from society (living people in pattern of social organization).

324. (p. 100) (MD) What is the distinction between the terms <u>culture</u> and <u>society</u>?

Major points: they overlap at many points; <u>society</u> refers to living people acting out a pattern of social organization; <u>culture</u> is a more abstract concept--the specific social heritage of a particular people (alive or dead); a culture defines the specific norms, beliefs, and practices of a society; it sets limits on the form and content of social organization within a given society.

325. (pp. 102-103) (MD) What do social scientists mean by the term <u>cultural relativity</u>?

Major points: standards for judging morality, truth, logic, beauty, and many other issues differ sharply from one society to another; this raises the problem of our own "absolutes"; while scientific sociology can never rule on the validity of any society's absolutes, it can point out the fact of cultural relativity and the need to take this perspective into account when evaluating a society.

326. (pp. 103-104) (LD) Discuss the term <u>ethnocentrism</u> as it relates to a major contemporary issue in American society (e.g., Gay Liberation, Women's Liberation, minority relations).

Major points: answers will obviously vary but essential idea is that ethnocentrism carried to extremes prevents peaceful interaction with different-minded groups, restricts innovation within group; however, ethnocentrism in limited form is a source of unity and stability within a group.

327. (p. 105) (LD) Describe the "ideal man" in Zuñi society, and indicate the implications this has for Zuñi culture as a whole.

Major points: noncompetitive; no search for personal power; emphasis on dignity, affability, sociability; this reduces conflict and aids in maintaining high level of cultural integration.

328. (pp. 105-109) (MD) Contrast the Zuñi culture with the American culture in terms of cultural integration.

Major points: Zuñi: highly integrated religious, family, and agricultural systems; noncompetitive; sociability is encouraged; consequently, high level of integration; American: culture more diverse in origins and based heavily on conflict between groups and segments of society; highly competitive and filled with contradictions--thus not highly integrated.

329. (pp. 109-110) (MD) Discuss the meaning of the _analytical_ approach to the study of culture. Illustrate in your answer the distinction between material, normative, and symbolic categories.

Major points: _analytical_ implies reduction to behaviorally meaningful units (traits), e.g., a wristwatch as a whole is a trait; its parts taken separately are not; culture traits can be classified as material (physical objects), normative (regulatory rules of all kinds), and symbolic (beliefs, legends, folk songs, etc.).

330. (pp. 109-110) (LD) Discuss the meaning and give examples of the following categories of culture traits: material, normative, and symbolic.

Major points: material traits: physical objects such as tools, weapons, clothing, etc. (examples will vary); normative traits: regulatory norms of all kinds--folkways, mores, laws, and all other institutionalized rules, customs, rituals (examples are legion); symbolic traits: more difficult to describe but includes all belief systems, legends, myths, folklore, and other symbolically expressed cognitive content.

331. (pp. 112-118) (LD) Discuss the role of subcultures in modern societies using the carnival as an example.

Major points: large number of subcultures in modern industrialized societies which serve to integrate their members; supported by the larger society; carnival is subculture with its own speech patterns, language, social organization, and ranking system.

332. (pp. 118-120) (MD) Identify five major types of subcultures in American society and give examples of each.

Major points: answers will vary but major subcultures may include: ethnic, racial, occupational, regional, religious, class, and deviant.

CHAPTER 5. Personal Organization and Group Experience

Multiple Choice

333. (p. 125) (LD) A more or less enduring organization of forces within the individual which helps determine consistency of behavior is called:
    a. a folkway;
    b. constitution;
  *c. personality;
    d. a drive;
    e. motivation.

334. (p. 125) (LD) All individuals have biological needs for food, water, etc., without which serious disequilibria occur. Urges to obtain

that which is necessary to correct such imbalances are called biological:
a. patterns;
b. urges;
c. pressures;
*d. drives;
e. inferences.

335. (p. 126) (MD) Which of the following acquired predispositions would be classified as a preference?
a. a desire for inner harmony;
b. prejudice against Cuban Americans;
c. acceptance of socialism;
d. being honest;
*e. an attraction to Cadillacs.

336. (p. 127) (LD) A set of evaluative beliefs concerning the acceptability of certain broad classes of objects, situations, or events is called:
a. a cognition;
*b. an attitude;
c. a preference;
d. motivation;
e. a habit pattern.

337. (p. 127) (LD) An individual has a relatively stable (acquired) predisposition to act and speak unfavorably on the issue of federal gun control. We would characterize this as:
a. a dysfunctional value;
b. a well-focused opinion;
c. a specific preference;
d. an unsound orientation;
*e. a negative attitude.

338. (p. 127) (MD) Milton Rokeach identified two kinds of values, which were called:
a. good and bad;
*b. instrumental and terminal;
c. real and artificial;
d. folkways and mores;
e. expensive and cheap.

339. (p. 128) (LD) The process through which an individual assigns meaning to sensory data is called:
a. affectation;
b. cognition;
*c. perception;
d. interpretation;
e. configuration.

340. (p. 129) (MD) Which of the following statements was made in the Tools of Sociology, "Validity and Reliability"?
a. measurement procedures which are unreliable may be valid;
b. all reliable measurements are also valid;
c. reliable and valid measurements are hardly ever found in sociological research;

*d. invalid measurement procedures may be reliable;
 e. a and d only.

341. (p. 132) (MD) Research cited in the text showed that rich boys and
      poor boys differed in their estimates of the size of coins. This
      finding illustrates the way in which perception is influenced by
      need. In other words the organization of a person's perceptions:
      a. is very important;
      b. is often incorrect;
      c. is different in rich boys;
      d. is measurable;
     *e. constitutes a system.

342. (p. 133) (MD) A conflict perspective on personal organization was
      advanced by which of the following theorists?
     *a. Freud;
      b. Festinger;
      c. Heider;
      d. Cooley;
      e. Mead.

343. (p. 133) (LD) According to the Freudian scheme, which of the follow-
      ing personality components represents the force motivating an indi-
      vidual to seek physical gratification?
      a. sublimation;
      b. ego;
     *c. id;
      d. superego;
      e. unconscious.

344. (p. 133) (LD) Instincts, according to the textbook definition, have
      all the following characteristics except which one?
      a. complex;
      b. inherited;
      c. unlearned;
      d. universal;
     *e. culturally conditioned.

345. (p. 133) (MD) Which of the following ideas would not be regarded as
      scientifically sound by contemporary social and behavioral scientists?
      a. constitutional factors influence personality development;
     *b. there is an instinct for motherhood;
      c. attitudes can be measured;
      d. aptitudes limit skills;
      e. temperament and energy levels vary.

346. (p. 135) (MD) Which of the following constitutional factors is not
      determined in part by heredity?
      a. aptitudes;
      b. temperament;
      c. intelligence;
      d. energy level;
     *e. all are partially biological in origin.

347. (p. 135) (LD) Among the following, which is a "constitutional factor"
      that can play a part in shaping personality development?

a. aptitudes;
b. intelligence;
c. temperament;
d. race;
*e. all of the above.

348. (p. 135) (MD) Which of the following is a constitutional factor which limits a person's ability to develop in particular directions?
a. cognition;
*b. aptitude;
c. perception;
d. habit;
e. all of the above.

349. (p. 135) (LD) Some persons seem to be limited by constitutional makeup in the development of certain common skills (e.g., in sports, music, etc.). This idea is discussed in the text under the term:
a. culture;
b. instincts;
c. intelligence;
*d. aptitudes;
e. sublimation.

350. (p. 135) (LD) Two people differ considerably. One is nervous, quick-moving, and responsive; the other is slow, calm, and delibera-tive. This is an example of differences in:
a. attitude;
b. instinct;
c. aptitude;
*d. temperament;
e. predisposition.

351. (pp. 135-136) (LD) The social process of learning to evaluate our own personal and social characteristics by interpreting the way others react to us is called:
a. self-imposition of norms;
b. significant interaction;
c. symbolic social behavior;
*d. "looking-glass self";
e. emergence of internal controls.

352. (pp. 135-136) (MD) Which of the following situations would be most likely to be a part of the "looking-glass self" process?
a. Walter accepts David as his friend;
*b. Jim notes that Lois rejects him and decides that it is because he is homely;
c. Betty finds Ted attractive and agrees to go out with him;
d. George and Mary become engaged;
e. Jo Ann decides that she can't stand Roger.

353. (p. 137) (LD) The distinguishing characteristic of human language-- as opposed to the language of other species--is that it is based on:
a. learned natural signs;
b. intricate biological mechanisms;
c. instincts;

d. heredity;
*e. significant symbols.

354. (p. 137) (MD) Which of the following situations would be characterized by the use of "significant symbols"?
a. a group of animals establishes a dominance hierarchy;
b. two insects fight;
c. two mammals cooperate;
d. one bird signals danger to others;
*e. two friends chat.

355. (p. 137) (LD) Symbols that are both arbitrary and conventional are
called:
a. coordinated meanings;
b. learned signs;
c. cultural signals;
d. communicative symbols;
*e. significant symbols.

356. (p. 137) (MD) Human communication:
a. is based on arbitrary and conventional symbols;
b. can take place only when the people involved have very similar
internal responses to significant symbols;
c. is the basis of the development of the "human nature";
*d. all of the above;
e. only a and b.

357. (p. 137) (LD) In Mead's theory relating "mind," "self," and the
symbolic processes, the individual's internal responses to self-
directed symbols were:
a. significant symbols;
b. play and the game;
*c. thinking;
d. gestures;
e. "looking-glass self."

358. (p. 138) (MD) In Mead's discussion of the significance of children's
play behavior, pretending to be mother punishing the child for a
naughty act is an example of:
a. generalized other;
b. symbolic interaction;
c. significant symbols;
*d. imaginary role taking;
e. "looking-glass self."

359. (p. 138) (MD) A child learns to grasp simultaneously the roles of
several others as they relate to his/her own in a group situation
(such as in a schoolroom). Mead's theory refers to this as:
a. symbolic role-playing;
b. role-playing;
c. anticipatory socialization;
d. significant gestures;
*e. the game.

360. (p. 138) (MD) Mead noted that children eventually develop the
ability to organize into a kind of system all the roles of others

around them and to derive from this concept a definition for appropriate personal behavior. This idea is referred to as:
   a. "looking-glass self";
   b. role complex;
*c. generalized other;
   d. play and the game;
   e. the "I" and the "Me."

361. (p. 138) (MD) Mead called the creative and spontaneous aspect of
the self the:
   a. Me;
*b. I;
   c. id;
   d. ego;
   e. superego.

362. (p. 140) (LD) Human beings who in early life are denied participation in group processes will:
   a. not be much different than those who have been more heavily in-
      volved in group life;
   b. tend to be rather shy and inhibited;
   c. make numerous mistakes in both grammar and social etiquette;
   d. be rather outgoing until they learn to respond to social control;
*e. show noticeable impairment in personal organization.

363. (pp. 141-142) (MD) The case of Anna was cited in the text. It was
clear that the child suffered from personality impairment. This was
a product of:
   a. an impoverished social environment in early life;
   b. inherited limitations on capacities to develop;
   c. an oversolicitous mother who pampered her;
   d. seeing too little of her father and brothers;
*e. both a and b above.

364. (pp. 142-143) (LD) Perhaps the clearest example of impairment of
speech process due to denial of group experience in early life (and
later rapid recovery) was the case of:
   a. Anna;
*b. Isabelle;
   c. René Spitz;
   d. the feral children;
   e. the ancient experiments of kings.

365. (p. 142) (MD) The case of Isabelle, cited in the text, shows the
effect of early isolation from groups. Intense group involvement
and intense training later in Isabelle's life:
   a. was inconclusive because she died;
   b. was of little use--she remained feebleminded;
*c. brought her up to a normal level for her age;
   d. caused her to become something of a genius, in spite of early
      deficiencies;
   e. enabled her to function rather well as a subnormal individual in
      later years.

366. (pp. 143-144) (LD) The data on long-term isolation of adults from
social interaction are less than clear. Observations of prisoners,

explorers, and others who have been cut off from society indicate
that:
- a. social isolation has little effect on adults--it mainly concerns children;
- b. such isolation often has favorable effects;
- *c. social contacts are important in maintaining personal organization as well as in forming it;
- d. social isolation has negative effects only on relatively weak individuals;
- e. social contacts make the individual more comfortable but less mentally alert.

True-False

367. (p. 125) (LD) Social scientists generally agree that the motivations of human beings all stem mainly from biological drives.
- a. true;
- *b. false.

368. (p. 127) (LD) Terminal values are enduring beliefs which surround the phenomenon of death.
- a. true;
- *b. false.

369. (p. 128) (MD) Research has shown that there is greater similarity between the properties of physical events and the way they are perceived than there is between the objective properties of social events and the way they are perceived.
- *a. true;
- b. false.

370. (p. 130) (MD) The basic cognitive structure of human beings is present from birth, rather than culturally instilled.
- a. true;
- *b. false.

371. (pp. 131-132) (LD) Dissonance theory differs from balance theory in that it attempts to relate consistency in cognitive dynamics to behavior.
- *a. true;
- b. false.

372. (p. 131) (MD) Balance theorists such as Heider are concerned with uncovering the constantly changing cognitive processes which underlie invariant surface behavior.
- a. true;
- *b. false.

373. (p. 133) (LD) Most social scientists believe that, although there is considerable conflict in some personalities, there is still a general tendency toward equilibrium or conflict resolution in the human personality.
- *a. true;
- b. false.

374. (p. 133) (MD) One important discovery of social science is that
     biological or genetic factors actually play no part in human intelli-
     gence, aptitudes, and the like--these things are all products of the
     social environment itself.
     a. true;
     *b. false.

375. (p. 133) (LD) Social scientists generally assume that, although
     humans are more intelligent than other animals, they nevertheless
     have instincts, as do other animals.
     a. true;
     *b. false.

376. (p. 133) (LD) The text defines <u>instincts</u> as behavior patterns that
     are unlearned, universal, and simple.
     a. true;
     *b. false.

377. (p. 136) (LD) The self-image which individuals have is the product
     of their involvement in groups, rather than an innate property of
     their own making.
     *a. true;
     b. false.

378. (p. 136) (MD) The term "looking-glass self" implies an ability on
     the part of individuals to see themselves as objects--that is, to
     see themselves as others see them.
     *a. true;
     b. false.

379. (p. 136) (LD) By the concept of "looking-glass self," we mean the
     reaction that people get when looking at themselves in a mirror.
     a. true;
     *b. false.

380. (p. 136) (MD) It is clear from the work of Cooley that a self-image
     gets fixed in the process of maturing and cannot thereafter be
     changed.
     a. true;
     *b. false.

381. (p. 137) (LD) When we say that symbols or signs are "conventional,"
     we mean that they are part of a shared culture and follow certain
     rules.
     *a. true;
     b. false.

382. (p. 137) (MD) Certain more advanced forms of animal life, such as
     baboons, have acquired the ability to use arbitrary and conventional
     symbols to communicate in much the same way as do humans.
     a. true;
     *b. false.

383. (p. 137) (MD) When we say that symbols or signs are "arbitrary,"
     we mean that humans have the ability to invent new meanings for
     symbols as they go along, thus making human behavior unpredictable.

a. true;
*b. false.

384. (p. 137) (MD) According to Mead, the "mind" is a set of response abilities acquired by individuals from social relations, rather than an innate property.
*a. true;
b. false.

385. (p. 138) (MD) According to Mead, the "game" which one begins to play as one grows up is an unhealthy, artificial, and neurotic personality trait, which one must lose if one is ever to be a truly self-actualizing person.
a. true;
*b. false.

386. (pp. 140-143) (MD) It is clear from the cases on record of isolated children that, although there may be certain kinds of social impairment, the basic IQ or intelligence is not affected, since that quality is inborn and determined by genetic inheritance.
a. true;
*b. false.

387. (p. 143) (LD) Social scientists agree that if individuals can engage in extensive social interaction while they are growing up, they will not be adversely affected by the experience of prolonged isolation in later life.
a. true;
*b. false.

388. (p. 143) (LD) Children who are isolated from other people will fail to develop a personality of a truly human kind, even though they do have the biological basis for such.
*a. true;
b. false.

Fill-In

389. (p. 126) (LD) Such general terms as generous, sincere, and pessimistic, as well as more scientific terms like introverted, masochistic, and inner-directed, are names for personality

_____.

traits.

390. (p. 129) (LD) If a measurement procedure produces similar results when repeatedly applied to the same people, it is said to be

_____.

reliable

391. (p. 130) (MD) A branch of social research in which the principal focus is upon the meanings of social interaction for the persons involved is _____.

ethnomethodology

392. (p. 133) (MD) Behavior patterns that are unlearned, universal, and complex are termed _____ ; while common among lower animals, they do not appear to be present in humans.

     instincts

393. (p. 133) (LD) In the Freudian theory of personal organization, the _____ develops through social learning and represents society's norms of morality.

     superego

394. (p. 138) (LD) That which is personal, unique, and distinct about individuals, that which permits them to be creative and nonconforming, is called (in Mead's theory) the _____.

     "I"

Matching

395. (pp. 125-133) (LD)
     drive   motivation
     predisposition   attitude
     trait   names pattern of behavior
     unconscious   id, superego
     habit   perception

396. (pp. 133-135) (MD)
     instincts   lower animals only
     constitutional factor   aptitude
     energy level   temperament
     preferences   specific tastes
     broad predispositions   values

397. (pp. 135-138) (MD)
     learning self-evaluation   "looking-glass self"
     internal response to self-   thinking
       directed symbols
     significant symbol   human communication
     acquiring human nature   mind
     internalized attitudes and rules   generalized others
       of others

398. (p. 138) (LD)
     creative self   I
     socialized self   Me
     internalized attitudes and   generalized other
       roles of others
     imaginary taking of role   play
     grasping all roles of group   game

Short Essay

399. (pp. 124-130) (LD) What are some of the more significant "components" of personal organization?

     Major points: motivation, cognitive structure (beliefs), habit patterns, character traits, acquired predispositions (preferences, attitudes, values), and unconscious processes.

400. (p. 127) (LD) What is meant by the term <u>attitude</u>?

Major points: a relatively stable tendency to accept or reject a specific, rather broad class of stimuli, such as a minority group, an economic policy, a religion, etc.

401. (pp. 132-133) (MD) What is meant by the statement that personality can be thought of as a "system"?

Major points: it is composed of interlinked components that have mutual influences on each other's functioning.

402. (pp. 135-136) (MD) What specifically is the meaning of Cooley's term "the looking-glass self"?

Major points: a set of beliefs and evaluations concerning the self that are derived from noting how others respond to oneself and interpreting these responses.

Broad Essay

403. (pp. 124-130) (MD) Social scientists refer to the "structure" of personality as being composed of certain interrelated behavior concepts. List as many as you can of those discussed in the text and define each briefly.

Major points: motivation--drives, biological and acquired, are based upon needs; cognitive structure--concepts and beliefs; habit structure--perception, emotion, thought; traits--both popular and scientific; acquired predispositions--preferences, attitudes, values; unconscious processes--much controversy.

404. (pp. 133-135) (LD) The text discusses the current scientific status of the term <u>human instinct</u>. What major points were made concerning this term?

Major points: this is no longer used by social and behavioral scientists; instincts in lower animals are unlearned, universal, and complex; human beings display no behaviors that fit all three criteria.

405. (pp. 135-138) (LD) Both Cooley and Mead stressed the importance of communication in personality development. What are some of the concepts they developed concerning these issues in their theories? Explain each briefly.

Major points: "looking-glass self"; play and the game; generalized other; "I" and "Me."

406. (pp. 141-143) (MD) What do the cases of Anna and Isabelle indicate?

Major points: they show the influence of deprivation of normal primary group involvement on personality development; case of Anna shows both physical and social disability; child progressed slowly; Isabelle had only social disability and made remarkable recovery.

CHAPTER 6. Socialization

Multiple Choice

407. (p. 147) (MD) People who are temporarily alone continue to guide
their behavior in terms of group norms. This indicates that:
a. people are afraid to be themselves even when alone;
*b. such norms have become part of their personalities;
c. Americans are members of a conforming society; they obey the
rules even when alone;
d. such people should try harder to be individuals;
e. conforming behavior is healthier than deviance.

408. (p. 147) (LD) Socialization is the process by which personal
organization is developed and maintained. It may be viewed as:
a. training;
b. enculturation;
c. controlling drives;
d. a and b;
*e. a, b, and c.

409. (p. 148) (LD) When individuals of any age come to accept as their
own a behavioral norm to which their group is committed, the norm
is said to have been:
a. individualized;
b. consensualized;
c. shared;
*d. internalized;
e. institutionalized.

410. (p. 150) (LD) Individuals belong to many groups. Sometimes the
norms of such groups are inconsistent, causing the individual to
internalize some but not others. This is called:
a. anomic selectivity;
b. focused learning;
c. differential institutionalization;
d. periodic reinforcement;
*e. selective internalization.

411. (p. 152) (LD) The view that human social activity is organized into
systems of roles is sometimes called the:
a. interlocking activity explanation;
b. division of roles theory of action;
*c. dramaturgical theory of behavior;
d. social institution theory of behavior;
e. socio-organic functional integration theory.

412. (p. 152) (LD) Early learning of attitudes and skills that will be
required for later adult roles is called:
a. taking the role of another;
b. preadult role learning;
c. prerole socialization;
*d. anticipatory socialization;
e. dramaturgical role adaptation.

413. (p. 152) (MD) Among the following, which provides the clearest
     example of anticipatory socialization into traditional sex roles?
     a. a girl building a sand castle;
     b. a boy viewing cartoons on TV;
     c. a girl learning to build model airplanes;
     d. a boy riding a merry-go-round;
    *e. a girl playing with dolls.

414. (pp. 152-153) (MD) Which of the following would be the best example
     of a "segmental" role?
     a. father;
     b. wife;
     c. child;
    *d. airline passenger;
     e. physician.

415. (pp. 153-154) (LD) The assumption of new roles--such as the change
     in sex identity experienced by Jan Morris--requires:
     a. reconceptualization;
     b. reinforcement;
    *c. resocialization;
     d. reconstruction;
     e. remoralizing.

416. (p. 154) (MD) One of the most important aspects of socialization is
     that group sanctions are internalized and become:
     a. periodic reinforcements;
     b. negative gratifications;
    *c. self-applied sanctions;
     d. positive sanctions;
     e. resocialized controls.

417. (p. 155) (LD) Group ranking systems are an important influence on
     personality because:
     a. they systematically transmit middle-class norms to all social
         strata in a community;
     b. they broaden the range of contact between members and create
         diversity;
     c. they are the source of the biological gene pool when people of
         the same stratum marry--thus influencing offspring;
    *d. they have the effect of narrowing the range of contact among
         members;
     e. they provide a tight system of social control--the upper strata
         controls those below.

418. (p. 155) (MD) The central value of the middle-class orientations
     and socialization practices in the U.S. appears to be:
     a. religious propriety;
     b. immediate gratification;
     c. individuality;
     d. occupational security;
    *e. emphasis on achievement.

419. (p. 157) (MD) In Freudian theory, one of the major socialization
     tasks of the family is to develop the child's:

a. id;
*b. superego;
c. libido;
d. "looking-glass self";
e. generalized other.

420. (p. 157) (LD) The most important group in all theories of the
socialization process is:
a. the work group;
b. the peer group;
c. the association;
d. the church;
*e. the family.

421. (p. 158) (LD) An emerging problem concerning socialization in contemporary society is the relatively limited contact young children
have with adult males (as compared to their contact with adult
females). This deprives young males of adequate:
a. social control;
b. role allocation;
c. subcultural development;
*d. role models;
e. learning capacity.

422. (pp. 157-158) (MD) Which of the following factors does not affect
the role of the family in the socialization experience of the child?
a. social class of the family;
b. occupational activities of parents;
c. parental attitudes toward child-rearing;
d. all of the above;
*e. none of the above.

423. (p. 158) (LD) The text maintains that the second most important
group as an influential agent of socialization is the:
a. family;
*b. peer group;
c. association;
d. community;
e. church.

424. (p. 160) (MD) David Riesman would classify the individual who looks
mainly to his or her peer group as a source for ideas and standards
of behavior as:
a. intra-group oriented;
*b. other-directed;
c. peer-socialized;
d. role-taking;
e. clique-emphasizing.

425. (p. 161) (MD) In the discussion of the so-called generation gap,
the text concluded that among the Hopi this "gap" is:
a. somewhat more severe than among the general U.S. population;
b. much more severe than among the general U.S. population;
c. about the same, since it is a universal phenomenon;
*d. not present in the same sense as among the general U.S.
population;

e. totally unknown, as the Hopi have no period of adolescence.

426. (pp. 161-163) (MD) The socializing experiences a child may receive in school include:
a. middle-class teachers and values;
b. student subcultures;
c. formal bureaucratic processes;
*d. all of the above;
e. only a and c.

427. (p. 160) (MD) Concerning the importance of the generation gap, the text emphasizes that:
*a. the family is more influential than the peer group in the decision to go to college;
b. the importance of the peer group as a reference group levels off or declines after college begins;
c. peer groups are more important for teenage girls than for teenage boys;
d. all of the above (a, b, and c);
e. a and c only.

428. (pp. 163-164) (MD) Which of the following best illustrates the concept of "incidental learning" from mass media?
a. a child decides he or she likes daytime serials (soap operas) and views them heavily;
b. a child learns how to count to ten by watching an educational program designed to teach counting;
c. a child views cartoons on Saturday and decides that he or she likes "Road Runner" best;
d. a child takes an interest in ecology and seeks TV programs that deal with this issue;
*e. a child learns about the duties, modes of dress, and social rank of a butler by viewing TV.

429. (p. 163) (LD) Learning about society can take place as an unplanned by-product of being entertained by mass communication. Social scientists call this kind of learning:
a. television socialization;
b. media knowledge;
c. communication socialization;
*d. incidental learning;
e. by-product learning.

430. (p. 165) (LD) Which of the following is an agent of specialized socialization?
a. a Greek Orthodox Church;
b. International Business Machines (IBM);
c. the Coast Guard;
d. AFL-CIO;
*e. all of the above.

431. (p. 165) (MD) The concept of the team-oriented person, as discussed by William H. Whyte, Jr., refers to:
a. a leader in a bureaucratic system;
*b. a personality configuration;
c. any member of an association;

   d. a person dedicated to a political machine;
   e. any of the above.

432. (pp. 165-168) (LD) Military socialization, such as that of the
      U.S. Marine Corps, typically involves:
      a. suppression of civilian identity;
      b. suppression of individuality;
      c. degradation of self-image;
      d. changes in the recruit's significant others and reference groups;
    *e. all of the above.

433. (p. 168) (MD) Which of the following statements expresses a point
      made by the text concerning socialization and adolescence in American
      society?
      a. for the wealthy, adolescence tends to end early;
      b. going to college, and especially to graduate school, is an
          attempt (psychologically) to avoid adult responsibilities;
    *c. "adolescence" can last into the thirties for some members of
          society;
      d. only a and c above;
      e. none of the above.

434. (p. 168) (LD) By comparison with earlier generations, adolescence
      for the middle class in contemporary America:
      a. is not stressful;
      b. is shorter;
      c. is about the same;
      d. is psychologically more pleasant;
    *e. lasts longer.

435. (pp. 169-170) (MD) Early female socialization in American society
      has traditionally centered around acquisition of adult roles related
      to homemaking and child-rearing. For some women, this fact appears
      to be related to:
      a. a tendency to return to the labor force during midlife;
      b. an attempt to find a basis for positive self-definitions;
      c. some attempts to reestablish the "glamour" roles of earlier
          years;
      d. expenditure of time and energy in club and civic work;
    *e. all of the above.

436. (p. 170) (LD) According to the text, many women in American society
      go through a "time of adjustment" after some years of marriage. This
      appears to be related to the fact that:
      a. a woman's physical attractiveness declines rapidly;
    *b. her roles as mother and homemaker decline in importance;
      c. she loses interest in sex at this time;
      d. her husband often becomes interested in other things;
      e. all of the above.

437. (pp. 171-172) (LD) Old age in our society, according to the text-
      book, brings which of the following tendencies?
      a. withdrawal from group involvements;
      b. loss of dignity and status;
      c. loss of meaningful roles;

    *d.   all of the above;
    e.   only <u>b</u> and <u>c</u>.

438. (p. 172) (MD) The major identity problem related to role socializa-
      tion for the older members of society centers around:
      a.   a declining earning power;
      b.   the loss of physical strength;
      c.   the end of interest in sexual activity;
     *d.   retirement from an occupational role;
      e.   withdrawal from group involvement.

True-False

439. (p. 150) (LD) When a person has truly <u>internalized</u> a norm, he or
      she will conform to it even in the absence of direct group pressure.
     *a.   true;
      b.   false.

440. (p. 150) (MD) In the process of selective internalization, an
      individual is usually influenced by secondary groups more than by
      primary groups, because of the formal kinds of pressures which
      secondary groups can bring to bear.
      a.   true;
     *b.   false.

441. (p. 151) (MD) One difference between "conformist socialization"
      and "deviant socialization" is that the latter kind does not usually
      involve the process of internalization.
      a.   true;
     *b.   false.

442. (pp. 148-150) (MD) Internalization of group norms can be considered
      complete when an individual comes to apply the standards of the group
      to him- or herself.
     *a.   true;
      b.   false.

443. (p. 152) (LD) The process of socializing individuals into roles
      often begins much earlier than when they actually assume the roles.
     *a.   true;
      b.   false.

444. (p. 152) (MD) "Anticipatory socialization" refers to the expecta-
      tions which parents and teachers have for the eventual success and
      effectiveness of the socialization process in their children.
      a.   true;
     *b.   false.

445. (p. 152) (LD) Learning new roles generally has the effect of chang-
      ing our behavior patterns, including our outlook on life.
     *a.   true;
      b.   false.

446. (p. 153) (LD) Resocialization is a process which takes place mainly
      in children, rather than in adults, since children have to adjust
      constantly to new roles in the process of growing up.

a. true;
*b. false.

447. (p. 154) (MD) In order for people to internalize the norms of their group or society while growing up, it is important that sanctions be applied to their behavior with great regularity--even to every act--if possible.
    a. true;
    *b. false.

448. (p. 154) (MD) Experimental studies of learning in animals demonstrated that behavioral responses on only an intermittent basis are particularly resistant to extinction.
    *a. true;
    b. false.

449. (pp. 155-156) (LD) An important consequence of group ranking systems for socialization is that people tend to associate primarily with other people of the same rank.
    *a. true;
    b. false.

450. (p. 155) (MD) During childhood and adolescence, the exposure of a lower-class person to the cultural norms of other classes is greatly limited in our society.
    *a. true;
    b. false.

451. (p. 157) (LD) An "agent of socialization," as described in the textbook, refers to any of the adults directly involved in rearing children.
    a. true;
    *b. false.

452. (p. 158) (MD) According to the text, the problem called "sex-role blurring" occurs mainly because modern women are increasingly taking on male roles.
    a. true;
    *b. false.

453. (p. 160) (MD) In a society undergoing rapid normative change, the "inner-directed" person is likely to shift his or her moral convictions to conform with those of whatever group he or she is a member.
    a. true;
    *b. false.

454. (pp. 161-162) (LD) One important consequence of the "neighborhood school" in our society is the tendency for the teachers in a given school to have generally the same kind of class background as their students.
    a. true;
    *b. false.

455. (p. 164) (LD) A study reported in the text concerning the effects of television on schoolchildren indicated that the children had acquired considerable information from TV about occupations otherwise unknown to them.

*a. true;
 b. false.

456. (pp. 165-168) (MD) Much of the pride and <u>esprit de corps</u> of
      Marines is a result of a careful and constant program of ego build-
      ing that begins with the new recruit.
       a. true;
      *b. false.

457. (p. 168) (LD) In modern times, the greater sophistication of young
      people indicates that the period of life called "adolescence" has
      gotten shorter.
       a. true;
      *b. false.

458. (pp. 169-170) (MD) In later life, such as middle age, women in our
      society are required to undergo rather drastic resocialization as
      their family duties come to an end; men, because of their greater
      occupational stability and connections, are scarcely affected by
      transitions of this kind.
       a. true;
      *b. false.

459. (p. 149) (LD) In a well-known laboratory experiment reported in
      the textbook, group pressures on individuals were found to be strong
      in <u>normative</u> matters, but they could not make individuals accept
      anything contrary to what they could see with their own eyes.
       a. true;
      *b. false.

Fill-In

460. (p. 148) (LD) The process of accepting a group's norms as one's own
      standards for behavior is called _____.

      internalization

461. (p. 153) (MD) Acquiring a new role, such as becoming a parent or
      taking up a new occupation, requires substantial _____.

      resocialization

462. (p. 155) (LD) The major theme stressed by middle-class socializa-
      tion patterns in the United States is _____.

      achievement

463. (p. 157) (MD) According to Freud, one of the most important social-
      ization tasks of the family is to develop a child's _____.

      superego

464. (p. 160) (LD) According to David Riesman, the individual who looks
      mainly to his or her peer groups as a source for ideas and standards
      of behavior is called _____.

      other-directed

465. (p. 172) (MD) According to the text, one of the major crises faced by the older person in society is the resocialization required in adjusting to _____.

retirement

Matching

466. (pp. 150-154) (MD)
selective internalization   differential association
anticipatory socialization   later adult role
dramaturgical theory   behavior as role complexes
resocialization   new roles
positive gratification   reinforcement

467. (pp. 155-161) (LD)
achievement motivation   middle class
immediate gratification   lower class
Sigmund Freud   Oedipus complex
other-directedness   peer group
youth cultures   generation gap

468. (pp. 160-170) (LD)
tradition-directed   primitive society
inner-directed   changing society
other-directed   peer groups
incidental learning   mass media
identity crisis   child-rearing role

469. (pp. 165-171) (MD)
team-oriented person   personality configuration
reduction of self-image   military socialization
· job security   lower-class socialization
identity crisis   occupational retirement
definition of situation   cultural norms

Short Essay

470. (pp. 148-150) (LD) What is meant by the _internalization_ of norms?

Major points: individuals learn a group's norms and make them their own as standards for guiding their own behavior.

471. (p. 160) (LD) What is meant by David Riesman's term _other-directed_?

Major points: a personality configuration in which the individual seeks definitions and cues for belief and behavior from others (mainly peers) as opposed to inner convictions or traditional norms.

472. (pp. 165-168) (MD) List several of the major features of the social-ization process used to indoctrinate military recruits.

Major points: suppression of civilian identity, limitation of individuality, restructuring of self-image, replacement of signifi-cant others and reference groups.

473. (pp. 169-170) (MD) The text maintains that the traditional female roles in American society contain the sources of a possible

identity crisis. Explain briefly.

Major points: early socialization prepares female for adult roles in homemaking and child-rearing; as children mature and homemaking tasks are simplified, the individual loses her main role links to others and thus her social identity.

Broad Essay

474. (p. 149) (MD) Discuss the main features of the laboratory experiment as a tool of sociological research.

Major points: dependent and independent variables; control of extraneous factors with an experimental design; use of control groups; advantages are high degree of control over extraneous conditions and precision of results; disadvantages—artificiality and limited applicability.

475. (pp. 150-151) (LD) What is meant by the "selective internalization of norms," and how can this influence a person?

Major points: internalization implies personal acceptance of a group norm; a person belongs to many groups, some with differing norms; the individual must internalize these according to some selective pattern; this leads to individuality.

476. (pp. 155-156) (LD) What are the "middle-class values" that play a central role in middle-class socialization patterns?

Major points: stress on achievement, postponement of gratification, rational allocation, upward mobility, self-reliance, worthwhile use of leisure, manners, courtesy, propriety.

477. (pp. 162-164) (MD) According to the text, what two major influences can the mass media have on the socialization process?

Major points: media distortions provide unreal definitions of the situation regarding appropriate behavior standards; incidental learning function implies that much information (perhaps incorrect) is picked up about society while viewer is being entertained.

CHAPTER 7. Deviance

Multiple Choice

478. (p. 175) (MD) The Mississippi alcohol laws, used as an example in the text, illustrate that:
   a. the law is actually a universal type of norm that serves as a clear guide to behavior for everyone;
   b. the law is ultimately determined by the outcome of court cases;
   *c. it is sometimes difficult to distinguish between criminal and noncriminal behavior;
   d. people need obey only those laws that are in agreement with their own personal principles;
   e. it is usually quite difficult to understand what a law is supposed to prohibit.

479. (p. 175) (MD) Whether or not a given act of nonconformity will be considered deviant is <u>not</u> dependent upon:
    *a. the extent of the division of labor in the group or society in which the act occurs;
    b. the tolerance limits associated with the relevant norm;
    c. the significance or importance of the norm to the group in question;
    d. the situation surrounding the act of nonconformity;
    e. the characteristics of the individual who commits the act.

480. (p. 176) (LD) The degree to which a group or society will tolerate acts of deviance is dependent upon:
    *a. the degree to which the violated norm is seen as important by the group;
    b. the strength of the religious traditions of the group;
    c. the extent to which sanctions have historically been associated with such deviance;
    d. the degree to which economic loss occurs because of the deviance;
    e. the degree to which establishment values pervade the ideology of the group.

481. (p. 177) (LD) A child who deliberately tramples a neighbor's prize petunia bed may be verbally reprimanded while an adult who deliberately does the same thing may be legally prosecuted for vandalism. This is the case because:
    *a. tolerance limits for nonconforming acts vary for actors with different characteristics;
    b. the norms governing flowers are not really very important in our society;
    c. children seldom really want to be deviant, they are usually driven to it by factors beyond their control;
    d. children are not held responsible for such acts in our society, so no legal action can be taken;
    e. our society values children much more than it does flower beds.

482. (p. 177) (MD) Mr. Smith, a black accountant, was picked up by the police on New Year's Eve for being drunk and was sent home in a cab. The following week, Mr. Jones, a black lawyer, was similarly picked up and was arrested for public drunkenness. The factor that accounts for this is:
    a. the social rank of the violation;
    b. the category membership of the violator;
    c. differential role behavior;
    *d. the situation of the act;
    e. the influence of informal ties.

483. (p. 177) (MD) A policeman stops a male youth under the influence of alcohol. If he is well dressed and pleasant, he is cautioned and sent home. If he is poorly dressed and sullen, he is arrested and sent to jail. This is an example of:
    a. illegal discrimination;
    b. selective sanctioning;
    c. police sensitivity;
    d. legal sorting;
    *e. differential treatment.

484. (pp. 177-179) (LD) An act that violates the norms of one particular group within a society may represent conformity from the point of view of another group. Sociologists refer to this as:
   a. selectivity;
   b. randomness;
   c. illogicality;
   d. immorality;
   *e. relativity.

485. (pp. 177-179) (MD) Concepts of conforming and deviant behavior depend on all <u>except</u> which one of the following?
   a. culture;
   b. subculture;
   c. time;
   *d. sanctions;
   e. they depend upon all of the above.

486. (p. 178) (LD) The wearing of wristwatches by men was thought to be a sure sign of "femininity" during the early part of the present century. Today it has, of course, no such significance. This illustrates the fact that:
   a. our standards regarding masculinity and femininity were simply absurd;
   *b. deviant behavior is relative with respect to time;
   c. our current perspective on wearing wristwatches is much more natural;
   d. tolerance limits vary concerning nonconforming acts;
   e. since the wearing of a wristwatch really has nothing to do with femininity, the norm had to change in order to reflect reality.

487. (pp. 179-180) (MD) According to the text, deviant behavior can have social consequences as well as consequences for individuals. In general, it can be said that deviant behavior:
   a. usually has negative consequences for individuals but positive consequences for groups;
   b. usually has positive consequences for individuals but negative consequences for groups;
   c. always has negative consequences for both groups and individuals;
   *d. can have both negative and positive consequences for groups;
   e. always has positive consequences for groups and individuals.

488. (pp. 179-180) (MD) The social consequences of deviance include:
   a. disruptive societal functioning and value conflict;
   b. group stability and cohesiveness;
   c. social and political reform;
   *d. all of the above;
   e. <u>a</u> and <u>c</u> only.

489. (p. 180) (LD) If people adopt deviant behavior patterns, it is quite likely that they are (choose the best description):
   a. clinically abnormal;
   *b. clinically normal;
   c. legally insane;
   d. neurotic;
   e. psychotic.

490. (p. 181) (MD) A young person joins a small group composed of people whose behavior and way of life is clearly deviant from the norms of the larger society. To understand or explain this, sociologists would focus mainly on such factors as:
    a. primary group involvement;
    b. subcultural content;
    c. personality defects;
    *d. only a and b above;
    e. all of the above.

491. (p. 181) (LD) The text discusses such deviant acts as sodomous rapes in prisons and concludes that such acts occur because:
    a. most prisoners are maladjusted and therefore tend to commit unsavory acts;
    *b. the organizational and subcultural features of some prisons are conducive to such assaults;
    c. prisoners are disproportionately drawn from homosexual populations;
    d. confinement in prison raises abnormal sex urges among otherwise normal people;
    e. prison officials encourage such acts as a means of keeping prisoners docile.

492. (p. 181) (MD) According to Merton's anomie theory of deviant behavior, which of the following is a major sociological factor in the etiology of deviant behavior?
    a. lack of motivation to succeed on the part of deviant persons;
    *b. lack of integration between culturally approved goals and means;
    c. inability to devise means to achieve success on the part of deviant persons;
    d. faulty socialization in the earlier years on the part of deviant persons;
    e. personality defects generated in the family setting on the part of deviant persons.

493. (p. 181) (LD) A general theory of deviant behavior focuses upon the relationship between goals that our society stresses and the means regarded as legitimate for realizing these goals. This theory is called:
    a. goal theory;
    *b. anomie theory;
    c. legitimate means theory;
    d. goals vs. means theory;
    e. goal/means discrepancy theory.

494. (p. 181) (LD) The concept of "anomie" in sociology is most nearly synonymous with:
    a. deviance;
    *b. normlessness;
    c. anonymity;
    d. mental illness or retardation;
    e. labeling.

495. (p. 182) (LD) In the typology developed by Merton to show the different "modes of adaptation" to a society's established goals and means, the mode most often selected is:

*a. conformity;
 b. retreatism;
 c. rebellion;
 d. innovation;
 e. labeling.

496. (p. 182) (MD) In the anomie theory of deviance, innovation occurs
      when deviant individuals reject which of the following aspects of
      their society's normative system?
*a. means;
 b. goals;
 c. sanctions;
 d. all of the above;
 e. only a and c.

497. (p. 182) (LD) In Merton's anomie theory, one mode of adaptation to
      society's rules is "overconformity," or "overcompliance." An example
      would be the bureaucrat who rigidly enforces petty rules as an end
      in themselves. Such behavior illustrates the mode of adaptation of:
 a. retreatism;
*b. ritualism;
 c. rebellion;
 d. rigidity;
 e. inflexibility.

498. (p. 182) (LD) In Merton's general theory of deviance, the hippies,
      drug addicts, tramps, alcoholics, and some psychotics would be seen
      as engaging in:
 a. ritualism;
 b. rebellion;
 c. innovation;
 d. maladaption;
*e. retreatism.

499. (pp. 184-185) (LD) An important question of concern in the labeling
      theory approach to deviant behavior is:
 a. how a group comes to define a given individual as deviant;
 b. how group members change their response toward a person labeled
      as deviant;
 c. what are the consequences on future behavior for a person
      labeled as deviant;
 d. what auxiliary traits are imputed to a person labeled as deviant;
*e. all of the above.

500. (p. 185) (MD) Shirley L. is generally regarded in her community as
      an alcoholic. Because of this, local merchants are hesitant to
      extend her credit, even though there is no real evidence of failure
      to pay her bills. In the labeling theory of deviance this illus-
      trates:
*a. the imputation of "auxiliary traits";
 b. the poor reputation that drinking can cause;
 c. the fact that alcoholism and untrustworthiness have been found
      empirically to be correlated;
 d. the fact that merchants are usually quite conservative;
 e. all of the above.

501. (p. 185) (LD) One of the important lessons of a review of labeling theory concerning general conceptions of the relationship between personality and sociocultural systems is that:
   a. sociologists have demonstrated that social and cultural variables are far more important in causing deviance than psychological ones;
   b. the genetic/biological factors that account for most forms of deviance are supplemented by sociological and psychological factors;
   *c. personality and sociocultural systems are both involved in explaining socially deviant behavior patterns;
   d. sociologists are reluctantly forced to admit that psychological factors may play some role in causing deviance;
   e. both b and d.

502. (pp. 184-185) (MD) Labeling theory implies that the system of inter-action between individuals and their community is restructured when they are stigmatized by deviant labels. If this is so, symbolic interaction theories such as those of Cooley and Mead would predict change in their:
   a. significant symbols;
   b. social ranking;
   c. natural signs;
   d. general intelligence;
   *e. self-concepts.

503. (p. 185) (LD) The perspective on deviance which stresses the importance of attachments and commitments to conventional groups is called:
   a. anomie theory;
   b. differential association;
   c. sociocultural learning theory;
   d. differential reinforcement;
   *e. social bonds perspective.

504. (p. 186) (LD) Sutherland's "differential association" theory in-cludes which of the following as important in the development of criminal orientations?
   a. primary groups;
   b. criminal subcultures;
   c. the socialization process;
   *d. all of the above;
   e. none of the above.

505. (p. 187) (MD) Which of the following is the best example of differ-ential reinforcement?
   *a. a heavy drinker moving to skid row;
   b. a depressed executive committing suicide;
   c. a drug user moving from marijuana to heroin;
   d. a demonstrator bombing a building;
   e. a juvenile who has no friends turning to delinquency.

506. (p. 187) (MD) The text discusses a variety of perspectives on deviant behavior--anomic, labeling, social bonds, and sociocultural learning. What do these perspectives have in common?

a. they are essentially based upon dynamics;
*b. they explain deviance in terms of interaction;
c. they are all based on exploitation of deviant individuals;
d. they all begin from the basic concept of normlessness;
e. they do not share anything in common.

507. (pp. 188-190) (MD) The text maintains that some individuals (e.g., homosexuals and drug addicts) can be both deviants _and_ conformists. This is possible because:
  *a. deviant subcultures permit them to conform to group practices which are deviant from the perspective of the larger society;
  b. they are not really deviants--the society simply regards them as such;
  c. they actually perform deviant acts on only a few occasions;
  d. police and other authorities do not adequately enforce the laws concerning such activities;
  e. the laws governing such activities are themselves bad laws and should be ignored.

508. (p. 188) (MD) Research on deviant subcultures has indicated that:
  a. deviant subcultures reduce stigma and societal reaction to deviant behavior;
  b. as participation in a deviant subculture increases, the likelihood for conformist behavior decreases;
  c. they are problem solving for those who subscribe to them;
  d. all of the above;
  *e. b and c only.

509. (pp. 190-191) (MD) Examples of "professional crime" would include all of the following except which one?
  a. confidence game;
  b. check forgery;
  *c. income tax evasion;
  d. counterfeiting;
  e. pickpocketing.

510. (pp. 190-191) (LD) The main example used in the textbook to illustrate professional crime was:
  *a. the "big-con" profession;
  b. racketeering in Chicago;
  c. petty theft in department stores;
  d. kidnapping in California;
  e. all of the above.

511. (p. 191) (LD) A distinctive feature of organized crime in comparison with other deviant subcultures is its:
  a. democratic nature;
  *b. division of labor;
  c. retreatist nature;
  d. immorality;
  e. supportive nature.

512. (p. 191) (LD) An example of organized crime would be:
  a. price-fixing;
  *b. distribution of illegal narcotics;
  c. confidence games;

d. burglary;
e. counterfeiting.

513. (p. 192) (MD) While pointing out some of the advantages and disadvantages involved in relying on official records for sociological
research, the textbook offers, as an example of a <u>successful</u> use of
such records, which of the following types of research?
  *a. criminology research;
  b. population planning research;
  c. alcoholism research;
  d. race relations research;
  e. educational research.

514. (p. 193) (MD) Among the following, which probably provides the best
estimate of the true crime rate?
  a. crimes cleared by arrest;
  b. number of convictions;
  *c. crimes known to the police;
  d. the index crimes of the <u>Uniform Crime Reports</u>;
  e. data on prison populations.

515. (p. 193) (LD) Our major source of information concerning the amount
of crime in a given area in the U.S. is:
  *a. the <u>Uniform Crime Reports</u> of the FBI;
  b. the crime data file of Yale University;
  c. the weekly sheriffs' reports from counties in the U.S.;
  d. estimates prepared by the U.S. Census Bureau;
  e. the statistics on crime published in the <u>American Sociological
Review</u>.

516. (p. 194) (MD) Which of the following factors has <u>not</u> contributed to
increases in the crime rate?
  a. better police record keeping;
  b. changes in the definitions of offenses;
  c. increases in insurance coverage;
  *d. reduced monies for law enforcement;
  e. increased anxiety about crime.

517. (p. 197) (MD) In the recent past, for both adult and juvenile age
groups, males have been about how many times as likely to appear in
crime statistics as females?
  a. about twice as likely or more;
  b. about three times as likely or more;
  *c. about six times as likely or more;
  d. about five times as likely or more;
  e. more than ten times as likely.

518. (pp. 197-198) (LD) There is a disproportionately high amount of
crime among:
  a. the young;
  b. the lower class;
  c. blacks;
  d. urban dwellers;
  *e. all of the above.

519. (p. 198) (LD) Police officers exercise immense latitude in deciding whether to arrest and charge juveniles and adults involved in crimes. This exercise of social judgment, which is based upon many nonlegal criteria, is called:
a. judgment selectivity;
b. selective perception;
*c. differential treatment;
d. police corruption;
e. enforcement flexibility.

520. (p. 198) (LD) About what proportion of prison inmates comes from the lower socioeconomic classes?
*a. two thirds or more;
b. about one half;
c. about one fourth;
d. more than three thirds;
e. about the same as from other classes.

521. (p. 199) (LD) Sociologists have come to which of the following conclusions about the legal procedures we now use to punish people for misdeeds (police, courts, jails, fines, etc.)?
a. such procedures ensure that the criminal element will think twice before committing offenses—that is, they reduce crime rates;
b. these procedures make certain that offenders are placed in situations where they can be reformed;
*c. it remains an open question as to whether this is an effective method for maintaining social control;
d. such mechanisms help restore the balance of justice by punishing violators;
e. as far as we know, these are truly effective in deterring deviant behavior of all kinds.

522. (pp. 199-201) (LD) Which of the following have been suggested as strategies for controlling various forms of deviance?
a. punishment;
b. diversion;
c. decriminalization;
*d. all of the above;
e. none of the above.

523. (p. 199) (MD) The reason most frequently cited for the provision of penal sanctions for violations of law is:
a. retribution;
*b. deterrence;
c. vengeance;
d. justice;
e. punishment.

524. (p. 199) (LD) The text suggests that the effectiveness of punishment in deterring deviance is still an open question. There is general agreement, however, that punishment and other formal sanctions will not be effective in preventing deviance unless:
a. all mentally ill people are committed to institutions;
b. substantially more money is devoted to law enforcement;
c. discipline in prisons becomes harsher;

d. more criminals are imprisoned;
*e. formal sanctions are supported by informal sanctions.

525. (p. 201) (MD) The current techniques used by law enforcement agencies to place some offenders into special programs rather than letting the law run its full course are called:
a. recividism programs;
*b. diversion programs;
c. plea-bargaining programs;
d. correctional programs;
e. none of the above.

526. (p. 201) (MD) Which of the following would be considered a victimless crime?
a. prostitution;
b. public drunkenness;
c. homosexuality;
*d. all of the above;
e. none of the above.

True-False

527. (pp. 178-180) (MD) One standard characteristic of deviant behavior, according to the textbook, is its negative and disruptive effect upon the group or society.
a. true;
*b. false.

528. (p. 178) (MD) Definitions of deviant behavior vary between and within societies. Among modern industrial societies, there is substantial similarity in the definition of deviant behavior.
*a. true;
b. false.

529. (p. 178) (LD) The concept of cultural relativity in the study of deviance implies that variations in norms may occur between subcultures within a given society, as well as between societies.
*a. true;
b. false.

530. (p. 180) (LD) One of the premises of the sociological approach is that most deviant behavior is attributable to people who are normal in the clinical or psychological sense.
*a. true;
b. false.

531. (p. 180) (LD) One point emphasized by the sociological approach to the study of deviance is the need to totally forget about the old clinical and psychological factors, such as individual needs, motivations, attitudes, etc.
a. true;
*b. false.

532. (p. 184) (MD) One effect of the labeling process can be seen in the fact that the occupational harm done to a worker is generally almost as great if he or she is merely accused of crime as it is if he or she

is actually convicted.
*a.   true;
 b.   false.

533. (p. 185) (MD) One of the implications of labeling theory is that
      stable enduring <u>patterns</u> of deviance may emerge simply out of inter-
      action between individuals and their society.
      *a.   true;
       b.   false.

534. (p. 185) (MD) A basic premise of labeling theory is that labeling
      people as deviant in effect assigns them a new role that will deter-
      mine the nature of their future social relations.
      *a.   true;
       b.   false.

535. (p. 186) (LD) The school has been identified as a possible factor
      in the development of juvenile delinquency.
      *a.   true;
       b.   false.

536. (p. 186) (MD) Research has indicated that the social bonds perspec-
      tive helps explain delinquency in America but that it does not
      apply to adolescents in other societies.
       a.   true;
      *b.   false.

537. (p. 187) (LD) One of the distinguishing features of white-collar
      crime is that white-collar criminals do not think of themselves as
      criminals.
      *a.   true;
       b.   false.

538. (pp. 188-190) (MD) Sociology has found that individuals who perform
      acts regarded by <u>society in general</u> as deviant will not be punished
      for their acts by the society if these acts were approved by a
      <u>subculture</u> to which they belong.
       a.   true;
      *b.   false.

539. (pp. 188-190) (MD) The interesting feature of deviant subcultures is
      that they both lessen feelings of isolation and reduce the stigma and
      societal reaction associated with deviant behavior.
       a.   true;
      *b.   false.

540. (pp. 190-191) (MD) Because "professional" criminals are so close
      in most respects to the "straight world," they are the likeliest
      of all criminals to be successfully rehabilitated.
       a.   true;
      *b.   false.

541. (p. 193) (LD) Research has shown that, while considerable variation
      exists in the discretionary treatment of deviants by the courts,
      there is almost no variation on the part of the police.

a.   true;
*b. false.

542. (p. 198) (LD) One finding of sociologists is that crime is the
great equalizer, since arrest rates are about the same across social
class lines.
a.   true;
*b. false.

543. (p. 198) (LD) Some white-collar crime is carried on in behalf of the
businesses concerned, rather than against them.
*a. true;
b.   false.

544. (p. 198) (LD) Sociologists believe that social class differences in
crime and delinquency rates can be explained almost entirely by
police and court biases.
a.   true;
*b. false.

545. (p. 198) (MD) According to the textbook, the disproportionately high
arrest figures for blacks are related only to racism on the part of
the police.
a.   true;
*b. false.

546. (p. 199) (MD) Crime rates are increasing in heterogeneous societies
because law enforcement officials cannot rely upon internalization
of norms as a means of social control.
a.   true;
*b. false.

547. (p. 201) (MD) Correctional institutions are, for the most part,
punitive rather than rehabilitative.
*a. true;
b.   false.

548. (p. 202) (LD) Punitive and rehabilitative policies for the treatment
of criminals are basically incompatible with each other.
*a. true;
b.   false.

549. (pp. 202-203) (MD) The newer community-based correctional programs
successfully combine rehabilitation with a punitive system.
a.   true;
*b. false.

550. (p. 203) (LD) Community-based correctional programs are not prevalent
because they have not proved successful.
a.   true;
*b. false.

Fill-In

551. (p. 176) (MD) The _____ _____ associated with any
norm can be exceeded either positively or negatively.

tolerance limits

552. (p. 182) (LD) The mode of adaptation advanced by Merton, in which
     there is a rejection of the goals and an acceptance of the means, is
     called _____.

     ritualism

553. (p. 186) (LD) _____ _____ theory stresses the
     importance of the socialization process in predisposing some people
     to criminal conduct.

     Differential association

554. (p. 193) (LD) The major source of information concerning crime is
     the _____ _____ __ _____.

     Federal Bureau of Investigation

555. (p. 199) (MD) Imprisonment, the most widely used sanction for
     criminal deviance, has been justified in terms of _____
     as well as deterrence.

     rehabilitation

556. (p. 199) (MD) The most frequent reason given for the use of punish-
     ment is _____.

     deterrence

Matching

557. (pp. 181-187) (MD)
     relationship between cultural goals   anomie theory
       and institutionalized means
     importance of socialization in   differential association
       predisposing one to criminal
       conduct
     definitions of deviance as a con-   labeling theory
       sequence of individual's behavior
       reaction subculture
     commitment to conventional groups   social bonds perspective
     importance of individuals or   differential reinforcement
       groups supporting one's criminal
       conduct

558. (pp. 181-184) (LD)
     accept goals, reject means   innovation
     accept means, reject goals   ritualism
     reject goals and means   retreatism
     normlessness   anomie
     reject goals and means but   rebellion
       develop new ones

559. (pp. 191-201) (LD)
     requires considerable training   professional crime
     operates over large "territories"   organized crime
     least stigmatized   white-collar crime

diversion   parole
victimless crimes   decriminalization

560. (pp. 197–198) (MD)

6:1 approximately	ratio of total males arrested to females arrested
4:1 approximately	ratio of blacks arrested to whites arrested
2:3 approximately	ratio of members of lower class to all other classes in prison
24 percent approximately	estimate of increase in total national crime rate between 1968 and 1973
25 percent approximately	estimate of American males who have had homosexual experience

Short Essay

561. (pp. 175–177) (LD) Discuss some of the factors that are important in defining behavior as deviant.

Major points: tolerance limits; differential importance of norms; situation of the act; characteristics of the violator.

562. (pp. 193–194) (MD) What are some of the difficulties associated with statistics on the extent of deviance?

Major points: lack of precise definitions, varying laws in political jurisdictions, operation of social control agencies, record keeping.

563. (pp. 193–197) (MD) What are the major sources for our statistics on crime and delinquency? Discuss each briefly.

Major points: Uniform Crime Reports by the FBI, and victimization studies.

564. (pp. 199–201) (LD) The justifications for the use of punishment in our society vary. Discuss three of the most frequent reasons given for its use.

Major points: deterrence, reformation, protection of society, retribution.

Broad Essay

565. (pp. 181–184) (LD) Merton formulated a general theory of deviant behavior which has provoked much interest among sociologists. Explain generally what the theory is about and then review his typology of "modes of adaptation."

Major points: describes relationship between goals and means in our society; typology should include discussion of conformity, innovation, ritualism, retreatism, and rebellion.

566. (pp. 181–187) (MD) Contrast the following theories and discuss any criticisms that have been given regarding each one: anomie, labeling,

differential association.

Major points: anomie: relationships between goals and means; quite general and simple; labeling: concerned with how the group comes to define individuals as deviant, how group members change their responses to the "deviants," and what the consequences are for future behavior of the "deviants"; remains controversial; needs to be worked into a theory; differential association: socialization experiences prepare individual to participate in an established criminal sub- culture; isn't considered to apply to all crime.

567. (pp. 197-198) (LD) Identify the main social background variables that are involved in differential crime and delinquency rates and explain why they are important.

Major points: age, sex, race, social class.

568. (pp. 199-202) (MD) Describe the general strategies of social control discussed in the text and explore their effectiveness.

Major points: punishment, diversion, decriminalization. Dilemma of punitive system versus rehabilitation has cast doubt on efficacy of correctional system as deterrent.

CHAPTER 8. Social Stratification

Multiple Choice

569. (p. 207) (LD) Max Weber amended the Marxist theory of stratification by holding that stratification was based mainly upon:
   a. class;
   b. status;
   c. power;
   *d. all of the above;
   e. only b and c.

570. (p. 207) (MD) Although status may be based on achieved characteris- tics, it is often based--in England, the U.S., and elsewhere--upon:
   a. social manners;
   b. proper speech;
   *c. family lineage;
   d. clothing style;
   e. conspicuous consumption.

571. (p. 207) (LD) In the study of stratification, the term status refers mainly to which of the following?
   a. wealth;
   *b. prestige;
   c. political power;
   d. pride of ancestry;
   e. refinement.

572. (p. 208) (LD) The most extreme form of a closed status system is the:

a. primitive society;
b. class;
c. association;
d. primary group;
*e. caste.

573. (p. 208) (MD) In a caste system a person's social rank is determined primarily by:
a. wealth;
b. intelligence;
c. age;
*d. birth;
e. none of the above.

574. (pp. 209-214) (MD) In comparing the class, status, and power distinctions between American and Communist societies, all of the following were conclusions except which one?
a. class, status, and power distinctions exist in both the United States and Russia;
b. discrepancies between the ideology and reality of classes exist in both the United States and Russia;
*c. China, unlike Russia, does not have classes;
d. the United States and Russia are characterized by linkages between class, status, and power;
e. all of the above were conclusions reached by the authors.

575. (p. 210) (MD) A pioneer in the systematic, empirical measurement of social class differences was:
a. Max Weber;
*b. W. Lloyd Warner;
c. Karl Marx;
d. Émile Durkheim;
E. Ralf Dahrendorf.

576. (p. 212) (LD) "The ability to make and implement decisions with or without the consent of those who will be affected" is a sociological definition of:
a. exploitation;
b. status;
c. prestige;
*d. power;
e. leadership.

577. (pp. 212-213) (MD) Among the following, which is the best example of power within the definition advanced in the text?
a. a general travels in an air-conditioned staff car, while enlisted men walk;
b. a wealthy industrialist buys a large yacht and builds a mansion;
*c. a psychiatrist refuses to certify that a housewife's emotional problems would entitle her to an abortion;
d. in the United States physicians are given more prestige than bookkeepers;
e. all of the above.

578. (214) (LD) Marx could best be described as a:

*a. conflict theorist;
 b. equilibrium theorist;
 c. neopositivist theorist;
 d. functional theorist;
 e. nihilistic theorist.

579. (pp. 214-216) (MD) According to the Marxian theory of social
     stratification:
     a. social rewards have been unequally distributed in all known
        societies;
     b. there is a continuing struggle between the social classes;
     c. the class in control exploits those below them, especially
        those without property;
     d. the family perpetuates the system by passing on wealth or
        property (or poverty and ignorance);
    *e. all of the above are true.

580. (p. 215) (LD) Which of the following is the most accurate defini-
     tion of Marx's concept of "class consciousness"?
     a. an understanding of a society's class system;
     b. a sympathy for the "underdog";
    *c. an identification with one's own class;
     d. a strong desire to improve one's own class position;
     e. none of the above.

581. (p. 216) (LD) The view that stratification has positive consequences
     for a society, and that differential rewards are given to those who
     play differentially important (or valued) roles in society, is
     called:
     a. role-reward theory of stratification;
    *b. functional theory of stratification;
     c. pyramid theory of stratification;
     d. conflict theory of stratification;
     e. the American Dream theory of stratification.

582. (pp. 216-217) (MD) Which of the following situations would be con-
     sistent with the functional theory of stratification?
     a. a bank teller embezzles a million dollars over thirty years and
        retires undetected;
     b. even a ditchdigger can invest in the stock market and become
        rich;
     c. those who gamble can sometimes win or lose very heavily;
    *d. physicians deserve the high status and income they have in
        American society;
     e. a humble factory worker inherits millions from his or her uncle.

583. (pp. 216-217) (MD) The functional theory of stratification:
     a. is probably more valid for modern industrial societies than for
        traditional ones;
     b. holds that stratification contributes to the normal condition
        of society and equilibrium;
     c. claims that working-class sons are as likely as middle-class
        sons to enter professional occupations;
    *d. only a and b;
     e. all of the above.

584. (p. 217) (LD) The functional theory of stratification appears to
     be most applicable to:
     a. a dictatorship;
     b. a caste system;
     c. a primitive society;
     d. a stratified society;
     *e. an open-class society.

585. (p. 218) (LD) The primary social agent for the perpetuation of
     class differences in America is the:
     a. school;
     b. government;
     c. occupational system;
     d. corporation;
     *e. family.

586. (p. 218) (LD) One of the social institutions taking an active part
     in altering parts of our stratification system is:
     a. family;
     b. legal;
     c. religion;
     *d. government;
     e. science.

587. (p. 218) (MD) It has been said that the family is "the keystone of
     the stratification system, the social mechanism by which it is main-
     tained." Which of the following statements lends support to this
     idea?
     a. intraclass marriage disrupts the stability of the family and is
         therefore dysfunctional;
     b. the majority of upper-class families are downwardly mobile
         after a short time in that stratum;
     c. the status of an individual's family has little relationship to
         occupational opportunities;
     *d. the class of an individual's family helps determine his or her
         opportunities for social interaction;
     e. all of the above.

588. (p. 218) (LD) Upper-class youth are more likely to succeed in our
     society than lower-class youth because:
     *a. they have more resources available and can thus bypass open
         competition in the job market;
     b. they have been raised with a minimum amount of conflict;
     c. low fertility rates within the lower class result in greater
         numbers of upper-class youth being needed to fill positions;
     d. the high rate of family disruption in the lower class prevents
         youth from obtaining the attitudes and values needed for competi-
         tion in the job market;
     e. upper-class youth are more talented and skilled than lower-class
         youth.

589. (p. 219) (LD) According to the text:
     a. formal education is limited to children of the upper class;
     *b. the quality of facilities and orientation to education vary by
         social class;

    c. a college education allows youth of all classes the same oppor-
        tunities and financial rewards;
    d. Russia is one of the few countries in which education is not a
        stepping stone to success;
    e. educational status has become less important with industrializa-
        tion.

590. (p. 225) (MD) The prestige hierarchies associated with different
     occupations have been shown to be:
 *a. similar from country to country and subgroup to subgroup within
      a country;
  b. quite variable in the industrial system;
  c. similar among developed countries but not among underdeveloped
      countries;
  d. similar among underdeveloped countries but not among developed
      countries;
  e. similar from subgroup to subgroup but not from country to
      country.

591. (pp. 226-227) (MD) The power individuals derive from their occupa-
     tional roles is:
  a. readily transferable to their families;
  b. dependent on how much they earn;
  c. generalized, in that it carries over into other areas;
  d. a function of their statuses;
 *e. most clearly delineated in bureaucratic organizations.

592. (p. 228) (LD) Which of the following is not one of the ways in
     which the U.S. government is trying to initiate social change?
  a. better voting guarantees;
 *b. school segregation;
  c. passage of minimum wage laws;
  d. the hiring of minority members in government;
  e. child-labor laws.

593. (pp. 228-230) (MD) The text reaches all of the following conclusions
     about social mobility and inequality in our society except which one?
  a. there has been a steady trend toward increasing equality in the
      distribution of society's rewards;
  b. the percentage of those below the "poverty line" is less than
      half as large as it was twenty years or so ago;
 *c. many Americans agree that the system works well for them;
  d. those who remain poor are poorer than ever;
  e. sociologists may have a bias in favor of the system because they
      are a part of it.

594. (pp. 230-233) (MD) Those factors which make possible significant
     social mobility in any society include all except which one of the
     following?
  a. geographical mobility;
  b. differential fertility among classes;
  c. differential socialization among classes;
  d. certain societal (cultural) values;
 *e. stable labor market.

595. (p. 230) (MD) The most important reason given for the increased
     mobility in our society is the Industrial Revolution. It has influ-
     enced mobility in which of the following ways?
     a. it has increased the size of the available labor force but
         reduced the number of jobs available because of specialization;
     *b. it has increased the number of white-collar jobs relative to
         blue-collar jobs;
     c. it has made intragenerational mobility increasingly common;
     d. it has led to increased specialization, which has made it much
         easier for individuals to set up their own businesses;
     e. it has established a stable occupational structure with a closed
         stratification system.

596. (p. 231) (LD) Horizontal, or lateral, mobility refers to:
     a. movement down in the stratification system;
     b. movement up in the stratification system;
     c. movement from one social system to another;
     *d. movement from one position to another of the same rank;
     e. geographical movement from one region to another.

597. (p. 232) (MD) Differential fertility may be a causal factor in our
     changing patterns of social mobility. The evidence gathered suggests
     that:
     *a. high fertility among members of the lower class impedes upward
         mobility;
     b. class differences in fertility will become more rather than less
         significant in determining patterns of mobility;
     c. members of the lower class restricted their family size, resulting
         in more upper- and middle-class people being able to fill the
         increasing number of jobs;
     d. fertility differences among social classes have had little effect
         on patterns of mobility;
     e. high fertility rates among professionals have resulted in some
         downward mobility for their offspring.

598. (p. 233) (LD) The changing role of women in our society illustrates
     that:
     a. education is an important agent of socialization;
     b. socialization may promote upward mobility;
     c. socialization may limit upward mobility;
     d. one's status and class may be dependent upon one's spouse;
     *e. all of the above.

599. (p. 233) (MD) The stratification system of American society has
     faced little organized criticism because:
     a. the upper class and those in power are the only ones capable of
         making their criticisms heard, and they would be the last to
         complain;
     b. the placement of token minority and lower-class persons in key
         positions has quieted the criticisms arising from those sections
         of our society;
     c. those occupying power positions have been recently recruited
         from the middle class--the result is little motivation to change
         the system;
     *d. there is little in the American value system to urge change;
     e. none of the above.

600. (p. 236) (LD) The findings of cross-cultural studies of mobility between the U.S. and other industrial societies of the Western world indicate that:
  a. there is much difference in the amount of mobility;
  *b. there is little difference in the amount of mobility;
  c. mobility is a function of traditional norms;
  d. Italy is the only country significantly similar to the U.S.;
  e. the net general drift was downward in most societies.

601. (p. 236) (MD) Lenski concluded from his cross-cultural research on mobility that the net general drift (after deducting rates of downward mobility) is:
  *a. upward in all societies;
  b. upward only in industrialized societies;
  c. downward only in less industrialized societies;
  d. downward in all societies;
  e. non-existent.

True-False

602. (p. 206) (LD) There is no known society that has not had (or does not have) some system of social stratification.
  *a. true;
  b. false.

603. (p. 207) (MD) A major contribution to stratification theory was Max Weber's recognition that stratification is based upon more than just economic factors.
  *a. true;
  b. false.

604. (p. 209) (LD) In societies like ours, the acquisition of status comes along automatically with the acquisition of wealth.
  a. true;
  *b. false.

605. (p. 209) (LD) When people in a society are assigned to status groups because of ascribed criteria, the society is said to have an open status system.
  a. true;
  *b. false.

606. (p. 210) (MD) Prestige can be changed only gradually, whereas economic position can change rapidly.
  *a. true;
  b. false.

607. (p. 212) (MD) Surveys have shown that most Americans understand pretty well where they stand in the class structure.
  a. true;
  *b. false.

608. (p. 213) (LD) Power is viewed as a reward of the stratification system and is used in determining the distribution of other rewards.
  *a. true;
  b. false.

609. (p. 213) (MD) Because of the extremely high cost of political campaigns, inherited wealth is a more important basis for power in
modern democratic countries than in traditional societies.
   a. true;
   *b. false.

610. (pp. 213-214) (LD) Contrary to popular myth, it is clear from a
study of the backgrounds of American presidents through history that
a person of lower-class origins has almost no chance of being
nominated for the presidency.
   *a. true;
   b. false.

611. (p. 217) (MD) According to functional theorists, even people in the
lower classes pretty much accept the stratification systems of their
societies.
   *a. true;
   b. false.

612. (p. 217) (LD) According to functional theorists, every society needs
a system of stratification.
   *a. true;
   b. false.

613. (p. 217) (MD) From the critical discussion of the functional theory,
it was concluded that it best fits those patterns found in the middle
strata of a relatively open society.
   *a. true;
   b. false.

614. (p. 219) (LD) Research reported in the text indicates that it
doesn't matter which college one graduates from; all college
graduates receive the same income.
   a. true;
   *b. false.

615. (pp. 222-223) (MD) Research on work motivation suggests that income
is the single most important factor motivating people to work,
especially at the top executive level.
   a. true;
   *b. false.

616. (p. 223) (MD) Statistics presented in the text demonstrate that
the money earned by chief executives of American companies is the
same in all industries but varies by the size of the company.
   a. true;
   *b. false.

617. (p. 224) (MD) Comparative rankings of occupations according to
their incomes show that the rankings changed very little between
1949 and 1959.
   *a. true;
   b. false.

618. (p. 225) (MD) Comparative cross-national research indicates that
there is considerable similarity in occupational prestige rankings

from one country to another.
*a. true;
 b. false.

619. (pp. 227-228) (LD) The government has clearly played only a positive
      role in modifying stratification patterns in the United States.
       a. true;
      *b. false.

620. (p. 229) (LD) Empirical data presented in the text show that the
      three kinds of mobility (vertical, horizontal, and geographical) are
      almost independent of each other in actual practice (that is, each
      usually occurs without the others).
       a. true;
      *b. false.

621. (p. 230) (LD) In past generations, much of the upward social
      mobility was due to the fact that the upper classes had fewer
      children than the lower classes to put into the labor market.
      *a. true;
       b. false.

622. (p. 233) (LD) The authors indicate that the chances for upward
      mobility of women in our society are helped by marriage but hindered
      by socialization.
      *a. true;
       b. false.

623. (p. 236) (MD) The authors conclude that, although the rate of upward
      mobility in the U.S. is generally somewhat greater than in other
      countries, there is a tendency for the rates to be similar depending
      on the level of industrialization in a given country.
      *a. true;
       b. false.

Fill-In

624. (p. 209) (LD) A society in which people can move up or down on the
      status scale, depending on their level of achievement, is said to
      have an _____ status system.

      open

625. (p. 216) (MD) According to the _____ theory, stratification
      has positive consequences for a social system because it reflects
      and reinforces the value system.

      functional

626. (p. 222) (LD) For the American male, and indeed indirectly for his
      wife and children, the chief source of income and prestige is his

      _____.

      occupation

627. (p. 231) (MD) Some theorists believe a core group of military,
      economic, and political leaders form a _____ _____

that effectively controls most important decisions in American
society.

power elite

628. (p. 231) (LD) Movement from one position to another, where there is
little or no change in rank, is usually referred to as _____
mobility.

horizontal

Matching

629. (pp. 207-212) (MD)
class   economic
social honor   status
party   power
closed system   caste
open system   mobility

630. (pp. 214-217) (LD)
conflict theory   class struggle
capitalists   owners
oppression   political power
proletariat   workers
functional theory   classes necessary

631. (pp. 218-228) (LD)
family   perpetuates class differences
school   sorts by life chances
occupation   major mobility vehicle
government   initiates stratification
                                  changes
agent of stratification   influences mobility prospects

632. (pp. 224-231) (MD)
industrial-agricultural revolution   stimulus to upward mobility
horizontal mobility   no change in rank
mobility prospects   socialization
revolution of rising expectations   drive for vertical mobility
occupational prestige scores   clear hierarchy

Short Essay

633. (pp. 207-212) (LD) Max Weber outlined three somewhat distinct
orders in society within which stratification occurs. Name these
and explain briefly.

Major points: class: basically economic stratification based on
life-style and occupational role or wealth; status: the prestige
or social honor people enjoy; this may derive in part from class but
it can come from other sources; party: mainly political power;
controlling decision-making.

634. (pp. 207-208) (LD) Discuss the difference between open and closed
status systems, then discuss the issue of whether or not our society
is truly as open as most believe.

Major points: open: people can move up or down in status depending on their level of achievement; closed: differences in prestige become so pronounced that they create closed status groups in which people must stay regardless of achievements; there are elements of a closed system in American society; religion, ethnicity, sex, lineage, and education all provide examples of areas that tend to preserve closed status systems.

635. (pp. 216-217) (MD) What are the central points of the functional theory of stratification?

Major points: in all societies stratification is related to the relative importance of roles to society and the rewards needed to ensure that people perform them adequately.

636. (p. 218) (LD) Briefly explain why the family is considered the "keystone of the stratification system."

Major points: class and status of family determine educational and occupational opportunities as well as opportunities for social interaction.

637. (pp. 234-236) (MD) Briefly summarize some of the findings on cross-cultural studies of mobility.

Major points: no great difference in the amount of mobility in the U.S. as compared with other Western societies; U.S. may be a little higher, but there's a tendency toward convergence based upon level of industrialization.

Broad Essay

638. (pp. 214-217) (MD) Compare the two theories of stratification given in the text, then, based upon your reading, decide which one (or possibly both) would best explain an open class society.

Major points: conflict: stratification is basically a mechanism of coercion; those benefiting from the system impose it upon the rest of society's members; functional: stratification is seen as essential and as one of the mechanisms that help maintain social stability; it rejects and reinforces the value-belief system; both are not mutually exclusive; from the book, however, the functional approach seems to be the best explanation for an open class industrial society.

639. (pp. 218-228) (MD) The text lists and explains four basic "agents of stratification" in our society. Name them and discuss the way each works in this respect.

Major points: family: primary agent for perpetuating class differences despite the fact that most families strive for upward mobility; school: designed as a social equalizer, but functions as a sorter, giving those who are academically successful better life chances; occupational system: main vehicle for upward mobility, but opportunities not open equally for all; government: increasingly active in removing mobility barriers, but has middle-class bias.

640. (pp. 228-234) (LD) Discuss some of the major trends of this century in social mobility in the United States.

Major points: increasing dispersal of wealth, prestige, and power, leading to generally increased equality; however, inequalities remain among the urban and rural poor; the latter may have even suffered downward mobility.

CHAPTER 9. Intergroup Relations

Multiple Choice

641. (p. 239) (MD) Dr. Jones, a black physician, is denied membership in the local Buffalo Club because its white members believe that all blacks have undesirable attributes. Sociologically, this is an example of:
    a. group rejection;
    b. normative cognition;
  *c. categorical treatment;
    d. dysfunctional superstition;
    e. stimulus generalization.

642. (p. 239) (LD) When specific individuals are responded to in terms of qualities said to characterize all members of a minority group-- whether or not the individuals have those qualities--sociologists note that they are victims of:
    a. group exclusion;
    b. minority categorization;
    c. segregated status;
    d. stimulus generalization;
  *e. categorical treatment.

643. (p. 239) (LD) The American belief that all individuals deserve to be treated on their own personal merits is contradicted by:
    a. ghetto development in urban areas;
    b. systematic prejudice against religious minorities;
  *c. categorical treatment of minority groups;
    d. all of the above;
    e. only a and c.

644. (p. 243) (LD) Scientific attempts to classify the races:
    a. are based upon improper criteria;
    b. are quite precise but too elaborate;
    c. are based upon cultural phenomena;
    d. are almost exclusively concerned with skin color variations;
  *e. do not necessarily shape cultural beliefs.

645. (p. 243) (LD) In many societies, people officially and unofficially employ which of the following types of racial classifications?
    a. genetic;
    b. morphological;
    c. anthropological;
    d. biological;
  *e. administrative.

646. (p. 243) (MD) The racial categories employed by laypeople may have
      little relationship to those proposed by scientists. Laypeople's
      classifications are in fact:
      *a. sociocultural;
       b. incorrect;
       c. overelaborate;
       d. oversimplified;
       e. semiofficial.

647. (p. 243) (MD) The chief factor that identifies an "ethnic group"
      and distinguishes it from other social categories is:
      *a. a sense of identity based on a common cultural heritage;
       b. spatial proximity or segregation;
       c. a common national origin;
       d. similarity of physical appearance;
       e. a common and shared language.

648. (p. 243) (LD) A category of people whose members are bound together
      by common cultural ties and who feel a sense of identity based upon
      common customs would be called:
       a. a cultural category;
      *b. an ethnic group;
       c. a folk society;
       d. a nationality category;
       e. a cultural race.

649. (p. 244) (MD) In which of the following societies would ethnicity be
      most important in intergroup relations?
       a. Eskimos in the Aleutian Islands;
      *b. the Soviet Union in the twentieth century;
       c. England in the Middle Ages;
       d. all of the above;
       e. none of the above.

650. (p. 244) (LD) Which of the following characteristics might provide
      "visibility" to a minority group?
       a. skin color;
       b. religion;
       c. language;
       d. clothing;
      *e. any of the above.

651. (p. 245) (MD) In earlier years American society treated many people
      of European origin as minority groups. The majority have now merged
      with the dominant population and ceased to be regarded as minorities.
      This transition would not have been possible if these people had the
      attribute:
       a. ethnicity;
       b. socialization;
      *c. visibility;
       d. categorical treatment;
       e. size.

652. (p. 245) (MD) The continuing struggle between America's ideals of
      equality for all and the hard realities of prejudice and discrimina-
      tion toward minority groups has been called:

a. the "Dominancy Syndrome";
b. the "Authoritarian Personality";
*c. the "American Dilemma";
d. the "American Inconsistency";
e. the "Peril of Our Time."

653. (p. 246) (LD) Many of the first blacks who arrived in colonial times were classified officially as:
a. freemen;
b. slaves;
c. soldiers;
d. heathens;
*e. servants.

654. (p. 246) (MD) Slavery in the New World:
a. was established initially by the Pilgrims;
*b. was given legal status decades after the first black people arrived;
c. was imposed by southern states after the nation was formed;
d. was actually never given legal sanction until just before the Civil War;
e. was part of the English legal system as far back as 1600.

655. (p. 246) (MD) Slavery was firmly established in the American colonies:
a. about the time of the American Revolution;
*b. early in the seventeenth century;
c. just after the war with Mexico early in the nineteenth century;
d. prior to the arrival of the white settlers;
e. along with the original Pilgrims.

656. (p. 246) (MD) The institution of slavery produced an elaborate set of roles, norms, beliefs, etc., that constituted the "culture of slavery." The importance of this was that:
a. it defined blacks as biologically, morally, and intellectually inferior;
b. it made it seem that blacks deserved to be enslaved;
c. it made it easier to deal with blacks as "property";
*d. it did all of the above;
e. it did only a and c above.

657. (p. 246) (MD) Slavery in the United States was officially abolished:
a. during the Civil War by Lincoln's famous Emancipation Proclamation (1862);
b. in the year 1870 at the close of the Reconstruction period;
*c. by the Thirteenth Amendment to the U.S. Constitution just after the Civil War (1865);
d. just prior to the outbreak of the Civil War (1861) by the U.S. Congress--an act that led to the Southern withdrawal from the Union;
e. during the Civil War by the famous Anti-Slavery Act of 1864 passed by the U.S. Congress in that year.

658. (p. 247) (LD) The great migrations of black people to the cities of the North were mainly a result of:

a.   the activities of the Ku Klux Klan in the South;
*b.   worker shortages in wartime industries and consequent economic opportunities for blacks;
c.   the special attraction northern cities always had for southern blacks;
d.   the Jim Crow laws of the North that opened education and economic opportunities;
e.   the lack of prejudice and discrimination in the North.

659.   (p. 247) (LD)   At the close of World Wars I and II the interracial situation in northern cities can best be characterized by which of the following statements?
a.   these were eras of expanding opportunities for blacks;
b.   these were times when blacks were pitted against blacks in a series of internal struggles for political power;
c.   these were periods when ghettos were burned by blacks protesting their situation;
d.   these were the most peaceful times in the history of American race relations;
*e.   these were periods of race riots that pitted blacks and whites against each other.

660.   (p. 250) (LD)   An apparently correct generalization about black/white conflict in the North from 1900 to 1950 would be that it occurred coincidentally with:
*a.   postwar readjustments;
b.   depressions;
c.   wars;
d.   inflations;
e.   political campaigns.

661.   (p. 250) (MD)   During the late 1950s and early 1960s the civil rights movement in the U.S. was based mainly on the concept of:
a.   militant resistance;
b.   gradual evolution;
c.   armed conflict;
d.   moral persuasion;
*e.   passive resistance.

662.   (p. 250) (LD)   The urban racial disorders of the 1960s differed from the earlier "race riots" in which of the following respects?
a.   they were not actual physical clashes between particular groups of blacks and whites;
b.   they were aimed at certain black leaders and policies, as well as white ones;
c.   they were more effective;
d.   all of the above;
*e.   only a and b.

663.   (p. 251) (MD)   Which of the following countries has the greatest number of Jews?
a.   Israel;
b.   Soviet Union;
c.   France;
d.   England;
*e.   United States.

664. (p. 251) (LD) Jews first began settling in America in:
     a. the 1700s;
     b. the 1900s;
    *c. the 1600s;
     d. the 1800s;
     e. the 1500s.

665. (p. 251) (LD) The Jews in the United States account for about what percent of the population (choose closest figure)?
     a. 1 percent;
     b. 7 percent;
     c. 10 percent;
     d. 5 percent;
    *e. 3 percent.

666. (p. 251) (MD) The first Jewish immigrants to the New World came from Spain and Portugal. They are called:
    *a. Sephardic Jews;
     b. Semitic Jews;
     c. Israelites;
     d. Old World Jews;
     e. Orthodox Jews.

667. (p. 253) (MD) The term Chicanos refers to which of the following?
     a. all Spanish-speaking minority people in the U.S.;
    *b. Americans of Mexican origin or ancestry;
     c. Hispanos of the American Southwest;
     d. recent immigrants from Cuba;
     e. persons of Puerto Rican birth or ancestry.

668. (p. 253) (LD) The largest segment of the Spanish-speaking minorities in the United States is composed of:
     a. migrants from Puerto Rico;
     b. the Hispanos of the Southwest;
     c. recent arrivals from Cuba;
     d. citizens whose parents came from Spain;
    *e. citizens of Mexican birth or descent.

669. (pp. 255-256) (MD) Among the following, which best expresses the treatment received by Oriental migrants to the United States?
     a. they suffered mild forms of discrimination at times, even during the present century;
    *b. they were abused, discriminated against, and banned by legal means for decades;
     c. there was some prejudice and discrimination during the last century (1800s) but not in more recent times;
     d. they were well received with the exception of the World War II period;
     e. they have always been admired for their industry and intelligence.

670. (p. 256) (LD) Japanese immigration to the United States began in substantial numbers:
     a. during the California gold rush of the 1840s;
     b. during the Spanish-American War;
    *c. at the beginning of the present century;

d. at the close of World War I;
e. at the end of the Civil War.

671 (p. 259) (LD) At present, the total population of Native Americans
     is approximately:
     a. a million and a half;
     b. three to four million;
    *c. just under a million;
     d. five million;
     e. about eight million.

672. (pp. 259-260) (MD) Which statement is true concerning Native
      Americans?
      a. they have never shared a single culture;
      b. the dominant American society and its agencies have never had a
          consistent and uniform policy toward the Native Americans;
      c. both whites and Native Americans are in a quandary about what the
          future of the Native Americans should be;
     *d. all of the above;
      e. only a and b.

673. (p. 261) (MD) A member of a dominant group deliberately does poor
      work or provides poor service for a client who is a minority member.
      This is called:
      a. manifest discrimination;
      b. latent prejudice;
      c. dysfunctional rejection;
      d. concealed hostility;
     *e. covert aggression.

674. (p. 261) (LD) A dominant group expresses its antagonisms toward a
      minority by maintaining a culture of jokes and epithets. This is
      termed:
      a. covert avoidance;
     *b. symbolic aggression;
      c. manifest discrimination;
      d. personal prejudice;
      e. total amalgamation.

675. (p. 261) (LD) Minority groups who have suffered segregation in the
      United States have been:
      a. Indians;
      b. Jews;
      c. Orientals;
      d. Spanish-speaking;
     *e. all minorities.

676. (p. 261) (MD) Movements such as the Zionist efforts to establish a
      nation of Israel, the migration to Belém after the Civil War, the
      back-to-Africa movement, and the Black Muslim philosophy are said by
      the text to represent:
      a. covert aggression;
      b. cultural pluralism;
      c. manifest amalgamation;
     *d. collective avoidance;
      e. prejudice in reverse.

677. (p. 262) (LD) In the United States, the pattern by which minority
groups have been expected to merge into the mainstream of social
life is:
  a. adaptation;
  b. amalgamation;
*c. assimilation;
  d. pluralism;
  e. homogenization.

678. (p. 264) (MD) The effort to "Americanize" immigrants to this country,
which was a popular policy of the early decades of the twentieth
century, represents the opposite of the concept of:
  a. socialization;
  b. assimilation;
  c. amalgamation;
*d. pluralism;
  e. homogenization.

679. (p. 266) (LD) Ed Smith concludes that he would accept a member of
minority group A as a roommate but not a member of minority group B.
This situation represents a difference in:
  a. personal prejudice;
  b. minority acceptability;
  c. discriminatory norms;
  d. scapegoating;
*e. social distance.

680. (p. 266) (MD) Which of the following types of questions are frequently
used by researchers studying attitudes?
  a. cognitive;
  b. behavioral;
  c. affective;
*d. all of the above;
  e. none of the above.

681. (pp. 267-270) (MD) The phrase "jew him down" is an example of which
of the following?
  a. neurosis;
  b. epithet;
*c. cliché;
  d. projection;
  e. scapegoating.

682. (p. 268) (MD) According to a table in the text showing social distance ranks for various nationalities in American public opinion,
those nationalities ranking highest (i.e., nearest the top of the
table) come from which part of the world?
  a. eastern Europe;
*b. northwestern Europe;
  c. Africa;
  d. Latin America;
  e. Asia.

683. (p. 244) (LD) Aside from blacks, who constitute about 11 percent of
the American population, our next largest minority group is:

a. Native Americans (Indians);
b. Orientals;
c. Chicanos;
*d. Jews;
e. Puerto Ricans.

684. (p. 244) (MD) Which of the following figures comes closest to that
of the black population of the United States?
a. 5 million;
b. 3 million;
*c. 20 million;
d. 10 million;
e. 30 million.

True-False

685. (p. 239) (MD) One necessary element in the definition of a minority
group is its relatively small size in the society.
a. true;
*b. false.

686. (p. 239) (LD) One consequence of minority position is the categorical
treatment of individual group members.
*a. true;
b. false.

687. (p. 241) (MD) At one time or another, all possible forms of
dominance over minority groups have existed in the United States.
*a. true;
b. false.

688. (p. 242) (LD) Since the dimensions of stratification are inter-
twined, once a minority group is able to establish a position of
economic strength, it improves its prestige and power as well.
a. true;
*b. false.

689. (p. 243) (LD) The "administrative" concept of race is about the only
form of that concept which sociologists still find valuable in their
research.
a. true;
*b. false.

690. (p. 246) (MD) Once slavery in the United States had been condoned by
law, it became a custom.
a. true;
*b. false.

691. (p. 246) (LD) One important characteristic of slavery in America
was its geographical limitations--that is, from the beginning it was
a strictly southern institution.
a. true;
*b. false.

692. (p. 246) (LD) From the sociological point of view, it would probably
be correct to say that the "culture of slavery" was caused by the

practice of slavery rather than vice versa.
*a. true;
 b. false.

693. (p. 246) (MD) The principal discriminatory feature of the "culture
      of slavery" was that it was imposed on blacks but not on whites.
       a. true;
      *b. false.

694. (p. 254) (LD) Unlike most immigrants to the United States, the
      great majority of Cuban refugees enjoyed middle- or upper-class
      positions in their native land.
      *a. true;
       b. false.

695. (p. 259) (LD) The American Jews of today are the only minority
      group which has never possessed a unified culture.
       a. true;
      *b. false.

696. (p. 260) (MD) Since American Indians have suffered such great
      injustices at the hands of the dominant group in the past, they are
      now united in their desire to be assimilated into American society.
       a. true;
      *b. false.

697. (p. 260) (MD) The nature of the relationship between a dominant and
      a minority group in a society is determined mainly by what the
      dominant group prefers.
      *a. true;
       b. false.

698. (p. 261) (LD) In American history, the forms of aggression occurring
      between dominant and minority groups have usually been symbolic or
      covert, rather than open and explicit.
      *a. true;
       b. false.

699. (p. 261) (MD) Open aggression is used primarily by a dominant group
      while a minority group usually acts out its hostilities through
      covert aggression.
       a. true;
      *b. false.

700. (pp. 262-263) (MD) Although the process of assimilation usually has
      taken two or three generations to complete, minority groups have
      merged into the mainstream of American life and have retained a large
      measure of their cultures.
       a. true;
      *b. false.

701. (p. 264) (MD) More and more members of minority groups in America
      prefer pluralism to assimilation.
      *a. true;
       b. false.

702. (p. 265) (LD) Because of their own suffering as a minority, blacks have been very much disinclined to show prejudice toward others.
    a. true;
    *b. false.

703. (pp. 266-267) (MD) Research indicates that members of minority groups and members of dominant groups rank all groups differently on social distance hierarchies.
    a. true;
    *b. false.

704. (p. 266) (LD) One of the difficulties in research on <u>attitudes</u> is that social scientists have not yet devised any appropriate way of measuring attitudes.
    a. true;
    *b. false.

Fill-In

705. (p. 239) (MD) The relative _____ of a group is not always a clear indicator of minority status.

    size

706. (p. 239) (LD) When an individual member of a minority group is automatically assigned qualities presumed to be shared by all the members, this can be referred to as _____ _____.

    categorical treatment

707. (p. 243) (LD) The concept of _____ refers to groups whose members are bound together by common cultural ties.

    ethnicity

708. (p. 261) (LD) When a dominant group maintains a culture of jokes and epithets which perpetuate its prejudices against the minority, they are said to be expressing _____ aggression.

    symbolic

709. (p. 267) (LD) Caricatures we hold of ourselves and others are called _____.

    stereotypes

Matching

710. (pp. 239-242) (LD)

size	is not a clear indicator of minority status
dominance	slavery
visibility	is essential for enforcement of unequal treatment
categorical treatment	individual is automatically assigned qualities entire group felt to share
exclusion	consequence of minority position

711. (pp. 246-256) (MD)
      due to political and economic   institutionalization of
          factors   slavery
      due to competition for jobs   black/white conflict between
          and space   1900 and 1950
      do not share a single culture   Indians
      place the greatest stress on   Jews
          education
      concentrated in California and   Orientals
          Hawaii

712. (pp. 260-264) (LD)
      symbolic   aggression
      Black Muslims   segregation
      retain culture   pluralism
      racial homogeneity   amalgamation
      aids in escaping prejudice   assimilation

713. (pp. 260-270) (MD)
      concentration camp   exclusion
      "melting pot"   assimilation
      Chinatown   pluralism
      Zionism   separatism
      epithets   aggression

Short Essay

714. (pp. 239-244) (LD) Define and discuss the major attributes that
      characterize minority groups.

      Major points: Answers should include definitions of relative size;
      dominance; visibility.

715. (pp. 243-244) (MD) Compare the concepts of race and ethnicity.

      Major points: race--we use the "administrative" concept of race;
      it follows historical usages of racial classifications; does not
      correspond to scientific classification; ethnicity--members of a
      group bound together by common cultural ties.

716. (pp. 260-264) (MD) Briefly describe the patterns of conflict and
      accommodation in intergroup relations.

      Major points: aggression: may be symbolic through the use of
      jokes and epithets, covert as well as overt; exclusion and avoidance:
      range from rigid segregation to discriminatory practices; assimila-
      tion: people gradually blend their differences; pluralism: main-
      taining cultural differences but still enjoying full access to the
      benefits of society.

717. (pp. 267-270) (LD) One aspect of prejudice is the development of
      unrealistic ideas about individuals who differ from oneself. Name
      and define three such types of beliefs.

      Major points: stereotypes--clusters of beliefs that are usually
      uniformly applied to certain groups of people; epithets--unflattering
      names which connote negative images and are deeply resented by those
      to whom they refer; clichés--slang phrases that tend to perpetuate

prejudicial norms; all three help support negative stereotypes and
maintain shared antipathies.

Broad Essay

718. (pp. 239-242) (LD) In the text, certain bases for designating a
segment of a population as a minority group were given. Name and
discuss these characteristics and then discuss two possible consequences of being assigned to a minority position.

Major points: attributes of minority groups are: relative size,
dominance, visibility; consequences of a minority position are
exclusion and categorical treatment.

719. (pp. 245-260) (MD) Contrast the historical experience of any three
minority groups in the United States, explaining how and why their
experiences were similar or different.

Major points: answers will vary according to which minority groups
are picked; they could include blacks, Jews, Spanish-speaking,
Orientals, or American Indians.

720. (pp. 260-264) (LD) Name and discuss four patterns of relationships
between dominant and minority groups. Illustrate each type of
relationship with examples from actual encounters between two such
groups.

Major points: aggression; segregation or avoidance; pluralism;
assimilation or amalgamation.

721. (pp. 264-271) (MD) Define and discuss individual prejudice and some
of the theories that have developed to explain its origin. Explain
why prejudice is a cultural phenomenon as well as an individual one.

Major points: individual prejudice is an attitude based upon antip-
athy; it is a rigid attitude with an emotional bias that's not easy
to change; cultural prejudice is part of the established or institutionalized culture of the society; prejudice is part of the folkways,
etc., that are transmitted to new generations through socialization.

CHAPTER 10. Social and Cultural Change

Multiple Choice

722. (p. 277) (MD) Which of the following is true regarding the effects
of the physical environment on social and cultural change?
a. it is the single most important factor associated with change;
b. it can only effect change socially and not culturally;
c. it can only effect change culturally and not socially;
*d. it may provide conditions that may be favorable to change;
e. it can in itself cause either cultural or social change to occur.

723. (p. 277) (LD) The text cites which of the following ways in which
the physical environment can contribute to social or cultural change?

*a. distribution of exploitable resources;
 b. wars;
 c. distribution of food surplus;
 d. population growth;
 e. lightning.

724. (p. 277) (LD) Certain categories of resources have led to change
     more frequently than others. They are called:
     a. liquid resources;
    *b. exploitable resources;
     c. facilitating resources;
     d. organic resources;
     e. inorganic resources.

725. (pp. 277-283) (LD) The textbook discusses all of the following
     except which one as factors which stimulate social and cultural
     change?
     a. the physical environment;
     b. population growth;
     c. ideology;
    *d. political development;
     e. leadership.

726. (pp. 278-280) (MD) Energy available to humans was greatly increased
     by:
     a. draft animals;
     b. rivers;
     c. wind;
     d. a and c only;
    *e. a, b, and c.

727. (pp. 278-280) (LD) An important early development which greatly
     increased the amount of energy available in society was:
     a. cooking;
     b. flying;
    *c. domestication of animals;
     d. invention of the wheel;
     e. solar energy.

728. (p. 281) (LD) Population changes have contributed to social and
     cultural change by:
     a. increasing the use of contraceptives;
     b. bringing traditional values into question;
     c. bringing changes in rates of marriage;
     d. bringing changes in ages of people at marriage;
    *e. all of the above.

729. (p. 281) (MD) Which of the following is true?
     a. since the total world population size was fairly small in the
        fourteenth and fifteenth centuries, a large change in either
        direction did not have much effect on social life;
     b. rapid population decline was only disruptive historically with
        certain kinds of ideology;
    *c. any significant change in a population tends to be disruptive;
     d. an increase in population size has been the only threat of dis-
        ruption to patterns of social life;

    e. today, research has shown that little alteration in patterns of
        social life has occurred because of population changes.

730. (p. 282) (MD) The main point of Weber's work on the rise of
      capitalism was that:
    a. Marx was wrong in assigning so much importance to economic
        factors;
    b. religion was more important than other factors in producing
        change;
 *c. ideas contribute to social change as well as derive from social
        change;
    d. adherence to other-worldly orientations fosters the development
        of capitalism;
    e. none of the above.

731. (p. 282) (LD) The impetus for social conflict and change, according
      to Marx, is provided by:
    a. political structure;
 *b. economic structure;
    c. rational capitalism;
    d. beliefs and values of society's members;
    e. ruling class.

732. (p. 282) (LD) Marx's ideas illustrate one of the basic principles
      of sociology. This principle is that:
    a. all sociological explanations are based on the economic structure
        of society;
    b. the revolution will come to all industrialized societies;
    c. ideas as well as technological developments bring about social
        change;
 *d. situations defined as real are real in their consequences;
    e. none of the above.

733. (p. 283) (LD) Examples of "charismatic" leaders would probably
      include all except which one of the following?
    a. Castro;
    b. Jesus;
    c. Mao;
 *d. Nixon;
    e. Napoleon.

734. (p. 283) (MD) Charismatic leadership is an important factor in
      bringing about change in that:
    a. it continues indefinitely;
    b. it usually brings social progress and improvement;
 *c. it usually arises when there are stresses and strains in the
        system;
    d. leaders of all social movements had the gift of charisma;
    e. it is based upon deep religious beliefs.

735. (p. 283) (MD) An attempt may be made to institutionalize the ideas
      of a charismatic leader. This may lead to conflict between two
      groups of people, as it did in Red China. Generally such conflicting
      groups are known as:
    a. proletariat and bourgeoisie;
 *b. bureaucrats and ideologists;

c. ideologists and bourgeoisie;
d. proletariat and ideologists;
e. bourgeoisie and bureaucrats.

736. (p. 284) (LD) Sociological theorists of the nineteenth century wrote extensively about societal change. For the most part, they stressed social:
a. structure;
b. conflict;
c. equilibrium;
d. intervention;
*e. evolution.

737. (p. 284) (MD) Which of the following ideas was a contribution of evolutionists such as Spencer and Marx?
a. change in societies follows a pattern of growth and decay;
b. societies become more complex;
c. there is no pattern to social change;
d. changes in a system have consequences throughout the system;
*e. b and d only.

738. (p. 284) (MD) For Karl Marx, the major social mechanism by which society changed from one stage to another was:
*a. class conflict;
b. natural selection;
c. increasing differentiation;
d. formation of new laws;
e. international war.

739. (p. 285) (LD) Ralph Linton's famous passage on the "100 percent American" illustrates the fact that many of our culture traits have been acquired by:
a. research;
b. invention;
c. stealing;
*d. diffusion;
e. folkways.

740. (p. 288) (LD) The meaning of diffusion is:
*a. the transfer of cultural traits from one culture or society to another;
b. the spread of evolution from one institution to another;
c. the spread of popularity or public acceptance of an innovative leader;
d. the increasing level of social and cultural differentiation;
e. none of the above.

741. (p. 288) (LD) The example given in the text of a culture trait that reached the Eskimos after it had passed around the world was:
a. jazz;
b. hula hoop;
*c. tobacco;
d. parkas;
e. steel knives.

742. (p. 288) (MD) A graphic way to depict or plot the spread of a given
     innovation through a population is known as:
     a. a borrowing curve;
     b. a fashion plot;
     c. an adoption plan;
     *d. a diffusion curve;
     e. a trait acquisition plot.

743. (p. 289) (LD) Which of the following terms was used in the text to
     describe the declining use of a culture trait in a society?
     a. displacement;
     b. retrofusion;
     c. infusion;
     *d. obsolescence;
     e. institutionalization.

744. (pp. 289-290) (LD) The decline of one cultural form brought about by
     the increasing adoption of a more effective functional alternative
     is called:
     a. exclusion;
     b. obsolescence;
     c. invention;
     d. substitution;
     *e. displacement.

745. (p. 290) (MD) The first people to try out a new trait in the process
     of diffusion are called:
     a. pioneers;
     *b. innovators;
     c. suckers;
     d. diffusionists;
     e. adopters.

746. (p. 291) (MD) According to the "exponential principle" in the study
     of social change, the number of conceivable inventions in a society
     increases very rapidly as there is an increase in:
     a. industrialization;
     b. the population;
     c. education;
     d. social heterogeneity;
     *e. the culture base.

747. (p. 291) (MD) The relationship between the number of traits making
     up a culture base and the number of potential new combinations of
     traits in such a base is:
     a. periodic;
     b. linear;
     *c. exponential;
     d. discrete;
     e. probablistic.

748. (p. 291) (LD) As the culture base in a society grows larger, the
     number of inventions potentially possible:
     a. increases steadily each year;
     b. decreases steadily over time;
     *c. progresses at an ever increasing rate;

d. shows very little change;
e. doubles every ten years.

749. (p. 295) (LD) Some years ago, William Ogburn noted that material
and/or technological aspects of culture change more rapidly than do
norms, beliefs, and values. He termed this phenomenon:
a. differential advancement;
*b. cultural lag;
c. trait surging;
d. technological lead;
e. material acceleration.

750. (p. 295) (MD) Among the following, which situation provides an
example of cultural lag as defined by William Ogburn?
a. the belief that the earth is round;
b. the old superstitions about breaking mirrors;
c. the change from diesel trains to steam;
*d. widespread prevalence of guns in an urban society;
e. all of the above.

751. (pp. 295-300) (LD) The various "agents of change" discussed in the
textbook included all of the following except which one?
a. economy;
b. government;
c. education;
d. religion;
*e. family.

752. (pp. 297-298) (MD) The example given in the text of a town which
declined as a result of an industrial change (Caliente) dealt with
technological improvement in which industry?
a. mining;
*b. railroads;
c. automobiles;
d. metals;
e. textiles.

753. (p. 299) (MD) During the last several decades, the federal government
has clearly been involved in activities as an agent of social change.
In earlier days, however:
a. it actually fostered more changes than at present;
b. it rarely fostered social change;
c. it never fostered social change prior to 1895;
*d. it also fostered social change;
e. there were constitutional provisions prohibiting government
involvement in change.

754. (p. 299) (LD) In the United States, the educational system is widely
thought to be an active factor in fostering social change. The text
maintains that:
a. this is correct, but mainly for schools in the northern U.S.;
b. this is correct, especially at the primary and secondary levels;
c. this has been true mainly for city schools;
*d. although it can create change it is mainly an agent of socializa-
tion;
e. schools never serve as agents of change.

755. (p. 299) (MD) According to research reported on in the textbook, education has:
a. increased students' consciousness of the milieu;
b. changed students' beliefs and values significantly;
c. refined existing values;
d. all of the above;
*e. only a and c.

756. (p. 300) (MD) Television has contributed to achievement of social change mainly by:
a. causing an increasing decline in cultural taste;
b. causing people to change attitudes;
c. creating new public opinion and even religious beliefs;
*d. the rapid diffusion of new culture traits;
e. stimulating large numbers of people to revise their sexual codes.

757. (p. 300) (LD) The chief impact of the mass media upon social change, at least up to the present, has been to facilitate the process of:
a. invention;
b. industrialization;
*c. diffusion;
d. obsolescence;
e. displacement.

758. (p. 301) (MD) The reason why the innovation of boiling water to limit disease in Peru failed was because:
a. even after boiling, the water caused disease;
b. the mayor intervened;
c. the elderly cautioned against it;
d. water is difficult to boil at high Peruvian altitudes;
*e. the traditional system of beliefs ran contrary to the practice.

759. (p. 301) (MD) In an example given of resistance to social change in a town in Peru, the ideas that made for resistance were:
a. traditionalism;
b. disbelief in bacteria;
c. a certain definition of boiled water;
*d. all of the above;
e. only a and c.

760. (pp. 300-301) (MD) All of the following are social and cultural bases of resistance except:
a. economic costs;
b. personal habits;
c. vested interests;
d. traditional beliefs;
*e. all of the above can be sources of resistance.

True-False

761. (p. 275) (LD) The terms social change and cultural change can be and are used synonymously.
a. true;
*b. false.

762. (p. 277) (LD) Most social scientists agree that social change can
ultimately be explained by one or another single cause, but they
disagree over which single cause.
a.   true;
*b.   false.

763. (p. 277) (MD) The physical environment cannot itself cause social
change; it can only provide conditions conducive to change.
*a.   true;
b.   false.

764. (p. 282) (LD) The authors of the text suggest that the real force
for social change in Marxism may have been the belief in it, rather
than its inherent truth or falsity.
*a.   true;
b.   false.

765. (p. 283) (MD) A new social, religious, or political movement continues to thrive only as long as it has charismatic leaders.
a.   true;
*b.   false.

766. (p. 283) (MD) Long-lasting social movements are unaffected by the
changes they bring about.
a.   true;
*b.   false.

767. (p. 285) (LD) The example in the textbook makes clear that American
society borrows from other societies primarily in the realm of ideas
rather than of material objects.
a.   true;
*b.   false.

768. (p. 288) (LD) A diffusion curve, according to the text, is the path
that a culture trait follows in returning to its point of origin.
a.   true;
*b.   false.

769. (p. 289) (MD) The term obsolescence implies that a given culture
trait has been completely abandoned by a given society.
a.   true;
*b.   false.

770. (p. 291) (MD) The "exponential principle" refers to the relationships
between the number of culture traits already existing in a given
culture base and the possibility of new combinations occurring at an
accelerating rate.
*a.   true;
b.   false.

771. (p. 292) (MD) Inventions and their general acceptance are more common
in societies with internal strains and stresses than in societies
free of conflict and turmoil.
*a.   true;
b.   false.

772. (p. 292) (LD) The government is increasingly initiating sociocultural change.
*a. true;
 b. false.

773. (p. 292) (MD) Since a government cannot "legislate morality," the activity of our government in civil rights has had very little impact on the racial folkways and mores in our society.
 a. true;
*b. false.

774. (p. 293) (LD) The example given in the text of London's "green belt" is an example of guided change.
*a. true;
 b. false.

775. (pp. 291-292) (LD) As a culture base in a society grows, the number of inventions potentially possible increases at an ever increasing rate.
*a. true;
 b. false.

776. (p. 293) (MD) In the Western world since the Industrial Revolution, a population "cycle" has emerged in which the most recent phase has been a reduction in birth rates.
*a. true;
 b. false.

777. (p. 295) (LD) The term cultural lag implies that the culture of a given people is rather primitive.
 a. true;
*b. false.

778. (pp. 297-298) (LD) One of the findings of the study about Caliente (the town that went into decline as a result of technological change) was that such an economic crisis could lead to changes in the basic values, norms, and goals of a people.
*a. true;
 b. false.

779. (p. 299) (LD) The government has been uniformly unsuccessful in its efforts at social and cultural change.
 a. true;
*b. false.

780. (p. 299) (MD) Government has the characteristic of fostering change in all other institutions except itself.
 a. true;
*b. false.

781. (p. 299) (LD) Since the government is the nation's largest single employer, it affects innumerable people when its programs are altered or recreated.
*a. true;
 b. false.

782. (p. 299) (MD) Empirical evidence suggests that, in general, students' values and attitudes do <u>not</u> change in college.
    *a. true;
    b. false.

Fill-In

783. (p. 281) (LD) A complex of beliefs and values providing an overall rationale for a society (and perhaps serving to delay or stimulate change) is an _____.

    ideology

784. (p. 284) (LD) The nineteenth-century students of social change, such as Spencer and Sumner, stressed, in one form or another, the process of _____.

    evolution

785. (p. 284) (MD) For Karl Marx, the basic mechanism of social evolution was class _____.

    conflict

786. (p. 299) (LD) Research evidence seems to show that higher _____ does not change attitudes and values for the majority of students.

    education

787. (p. 300) (MD) The mass media has mediated social change by the process of _____.

    diffusion

788. (p. 300) (MD) Resistance to change becomes most pronounced when _____ values and beliefs are involved.

    traditional

Matching

789. (pp. 275-283) (LD)
    cultural change   new traits
    social change   altered roles and norms
    physical environment   stimulating factor
    population change   disruptive factor
    charisma   leadership

790. (pp. 283-290) (MD)
    folkways   institutionalized
    spread of innovation   diffusion curve
    abandonment of culture trait   obsolescence
    fad   limited adoption
    displacement   functional alternative

791 (pp. 295-299) (LD)
    Caliente   technological change in
                                          railroads
    Galena, Ill.   railroads rejected

federal government
education
religion as agent of change

increasing as agent of change
agent of socialization
depends on cultural variables

792. (pp. 300-302) (MD)
television
fear
resistance to change
Peruvian village
overcoming resistance

diffusion
resistance to change
traditional values
rejected innovation
group decision

Short Essay

793. (p. 282) (MD) Can the values, beliefs, and ideas of a society provide impetus for change according to Marx? According to Weber?
Explain.

Major points: Marx: it is the economic structure of a society that
stimulates change, not the values and ideas of the society; social
existence determines consciousness; Weber: ideas as well as technological developments and economic structure can be stimulating
factors; he used Puritan Ethic and linked it to economic change.

794. (pp. 288-290) (LD) Briefly describe the characteristic pattern
followed when a new culture trait or complex is introduced to a
group and eventually becomes adopted.

Major points: innovators: early adopters; majority of the group:
late adopters.

795. (pp. 297-298) (LD) The case of Caliente was cited in the text as an
example of change due to the economic institution acting as agent
of change. Explain briefly.

Major points: the railroad changed from steam to diesel; this altered
the economic base of the community, which then tried unsuccessfully
to adapt to a new situation; the town declined sharply.

796. (pp. 300-302) (MD) Describe several sources of resistance to change.

Major points: traditional values, fear, costs of accepting change,
attitudes, etc., may be given.

Broad Essay

797. (pp. 277-283) (LD) At least four factors thought by sociologists to
stimulate social change were mentioned in the text. Name these and
explain each very briefly.

Major points: physical environment: exploitable resources, energy
sets limits on what people can do and how their society is organized;
population growth or decline: often requires social and/or cultural
adaptations; ideologies, such as Marxism or the Protestant Ethic often
underlie changing social and cultural arrangements; leadership,
especially charismatic leadership, can be a stimulant to change;
all four can be linked.

798. (pp. 283-293) (MD) Mention and define three major patterns of change that occur in society.

Major points: evolution: nineteenth-century concept based on the idea of increasing complexity and perfection of social order; diffusion: both intersocietal and intrasocietal adoption of traits leads to the spread of culture traits and new organizational components; invention: potentially based upon exponential principle, leads to increased number of traits in a culture.

799. (pp. 295-300) (MD) Name and explain why each of the four agents of cultural change given in the book are central in initiating and directing social change.

Major points: economy: technological change has had repercussions throughout all parts of our society, both positive and negative; often it has unforeseen effects; government: it fosters change in many areas that closely affect individuals, as health, welfare, etc.; it also is the largest single employer in the country; education: centers for socialization and change which help to make individuals become functioning parts of society; mass media, particularly television, has played an important role in stimulating and fostering social change.

800. (pp. 300-302) (LD) Explain some of the social and cultural bases of resistance to change and give some examples.

Major points: resistance to change can come from traditional values, economic costs, individual factors such as personal habits, attitudes, and other predispositions, as well as other cultural beliefs; examples include the Peruvian village which resisted hygienic measures, the pain killer Analoze, and many others.

CHAPTER 11. Demographic Change

Multiple Choice

801. (p. 304) (MD) Estimates indicate that if current trends continue, the world's population will double:
   *a. in less than fifty years;
    b. in five hundred years;
    c. in five years;
    d. in five thousand years;
    e. in fifty thousand years.

802. (p. 305) (LD) The world's population is currently growing at a rate faster than ever before in history. The rate now is about:
    a. 5 percent per year;
   *b. 2 percent per year;
    c. 10 percent per year;
    d. less than 1 percent per year;
    e. about 100 percent per decade.

803. (p. 305) (MD) Among the following, which statement is most consistent with Malthus's theory of population growth:

*a. populations tend to grow by geometric progression--food supply can increase only arithmetically;

b. population grows somewhat faster than food supply--especially when droughts occur;

c. the populations of Asia grow so rapidly that they threaten to overwhelm the world;

d. food supply grows in an exponential manner while population growth is linear;

e. historically, famine, war, and plague have served as preventative checks on population.

804. (p. 306) (LD) Malthus maintained that wars, famine, and plague have served historically as:
a. alternatives to birth control;
b. moral checks on culture growth;
c. selection factors improving the race;
d. neopositivistic stimuli to science;
*e. positive checks on population.

805. (pp. 306-307) (MD) The text discusses several weaknesses of Malthus' theory of population. They do not include the fact that:
a. social and cultural change were not taken into account;
b. the biological drive for sexual gratification was overestimated;
c. revolutionary agricultural developments were not foreseen;
d. the mathematics of his theory were faulty;
*e. b and d only.

806. (pp. 306-307) (MD) The prophecies of Malthus about population growth have failed to come true in societies like our own because of:
a. changing moral and religious views on sex;
b. development of contraceptives;
c. new agricultural techniques;
*d. all of the above;
e. only b and c.

807. (p. 307) (LD) The demographic transition refers to a situation in which:
*a. high mortality and fertility rates change to low mortality and fertility rates;
b. both mortality and fertility rates increase substantially;
c. high mortality rates decline while the fertility rate is constant;
d. high fertility rates decline while mortality rates are constant;
e. the mortality rate is replaced by the fertility rate.

808. (p. 307) (LD) The statistical study of populations, their size, composition, and distribution, is called:
a. ethnography;
b. ethnology;
c. sociography;
d. censusology;
*e. demography.

809. (p. 307) (MD) Which of the following terms refers to the biological capacity for producing offspring in a given population?
*a. fecundity;
b. fertility;

c. infant mortality;
d. birth rate;
e. natural growth.

810. (p. 307) (MD) The number of infants who die in their first year of life per 1000 live births is called the:
a. child death rate;
*b. infant mortality rate;
c. first year death rate;
d. first year mortality rate;
e. child mortality rate.

811. (p. 308) (LD) The "demographic transition" discussed in the textbook began mainly as a result of:
a. spreading literacy;
b. devastating wars;
*c. the Industrial Revolution;
d. changing family norms;
e. all of the above.

812. (p. 308) (MD) According to the theory of demographic transition, the population of a highly industrialized country would be characterized by:
a. lowering death rates but high birth rates;
*b. low death rates and low birth rates;
c. high death rates but low birth rates;
d. high birth rates but low death rates;
e. rising birth rates and lowering death rates.

813. (p. 310) (MD) A conclusion reached in the text is that the developing nations are undergoing a "population explosion." The major reason for this is:
a. increased life expectancy;
b. increased birth rate;
c. absence of wars, famine, and plagues;
*d. reduction in infant mortality;
e. migration into developing nations.

814. (p. 310) (MD) Which of the following statements would be true concerning the comparative population growth rates of developed and underdeveloped countries?
a. the rate has been decreasing in developed countries, but increasing in underdeveloped ones;
*b. the rate has been increasing in both kinds of countries, but faster in underdeveloped ones;
c. the rate has been increasing faster in developed countries than in underdeveloped ones;
d. the rates have remained about the same lately in both kinds of countries;
e. none of the above.

815. (p. 311) (LD) The chief obstacle still remaining to effective population control programs in the so-called developing countries is which of the following?
*a. traditional beliefs about sex, family, and sex roles;
b. mothers simply continue to prefer large families;

    c. contraceptive devices are not available;
    d. illiteracy;
    e. low levels of medical knowledge.

816. (pp. 312-313) (MD) In comparing current population trends in Latin America with historical ones in the United States, the authors observe that:
    a. the current population growth rate in Latin America is about the same as in the United States between 1790 and 1860;
    b. like the United States in its early history, Latin America has a considerable amount of unused farmland;
    c. like the United States in its early history, Latin America is experiencing a large-scale migration of its people to new farmlands;
    d. all of the above;
  *e. only a and b.

817. (pp. 312-314) (LD) One of the real problems facing the so-called developing nations is:
    a. urban concentration;
    b. an excessive burden of child dependency;
    c. labor force of high density;
    d. lack of investment capital;
  *e. all of the above.

818. (p. 316) (LD) Since the beginning of the present century, Mexico's population has:
    a. doubled;
    b. tripled;
  *c. quadrupled;
    d. grown by half;
    e. stayed about the same.

819. (p. 317) (LD) In Mexico, a large proportion of the population is under 15 years of age. In terms of education this means that:
    a. there has been little progress in combating illiteracy; few schools have been built in 20 years;
  *b. the Mexican government has had to allocate 15 to 20 percent of its resources to education;
    c. the Mexican government is largely indifferent to the problem;
    d. there will be no problem--access to schools is about the same as in the United States;
    e. with a declining birth rate, the problem of illiteracy will soon disappear.

820. (p. 317) (MD) Which of the following is true regarding illiteracy in Mexico?
    a. the proportion of illiterate Mexicans has grown steadily smaller;
    b. the number of illiterate Mexicans has remained the same;
    c. future reduction in illiteracy seems to depend upon future reduction in birth rate;
  *d. all of the above;
    e. only b and c.

821. (p. 318) (MD) The current situation regarding birth control in Mexico indicates that:

a. many Mexicans are acutely aware of the hardships posed by too
    many children;
b. Mexican bishops support birth control;
c. the Mexican government has shown itself to be in favor of
    family planning;
d. only a and c above are true;
*e. a, b, and c above are all true.

822. (p. 318) (LD) The textbook estimates the present population of main-
      land China at about:
      a. 200 million;
      *b. 800 million;
      c. 400 million;
      d. 500 million;
      e. 600 million.

823. (p. 318) (LD) When Chinese Communists took over in 1949, a large
      segment of the population was required to produce the food supply.
      The text estimates this as:
      a. 15 percent;
      *b. 85 percent;
      c. 45 percent;
      d. 65 percent;
      e. 25 percent.

824. (p. 319) (MD) The efforts of the Communist regime in China to destroy
      the traditional clan structure have had a number of consequences,
      including which of the following?
      *a. they have made family life in modern China more like that in the
           industrialized West;
      b. they have increased industrial output;
      c. they have had little impact on traditional Chinese family
          structure;
      d. none of the above;
      e. only b and c.

825. (p. 322) (MD) The political leaders of China faced the problem of a
      rapidly growing population and a preindustrial food production system.
      Their response to this was to:
      a. accept the Malthusian arguments and concentrate on family planning
          since 1949;
      b. ignore the Malthusian arguments and strengthen the clan system
          so as to bolster food production;
      c. recognize the validity of the Malthusian arguments and reduce
          efforts to industrialize in order to concentrate on farming;
      *d. reject the Malthusian arguments and try to reorganize the
           economic system;
      e. eliminate population through repressive measures.

826. (p. 322) (LD) At the time China launched its "Great Leap Forward" in
      1958 it took the following position on birth control:
      a. it put into effect a rigid program of birth control;
      *b. it announced that population growth was a creative force;
      c. it advocated birth control mainly for rural families;
      d. it found justification for strong birth control measures in the
          writings of Mao;

e. it did both a and c.

827. (p. 323) LD)   At present, China is advocating:
  a. a rigidly enforced system of birth control by abortions;
  b. unregulated population growth;
  c. a doubling of population in ten years by providing incentives for large families;
  *d. planned parenthood;
  e. widespread illegitimacy as a means of disrupting the old family and clan system.

828. (p. 324) (MD)   For sampling and research purposes, the most important feature of the census unit known as a "census tract" is its:
  a. large size;
  *b. social and/or geographical homogeneity;
  c. population size;
  d. legal basis;
  e. all of the above.

829. (p. 325) (LD)   Among the sociological lessons to be obtained from a review of the demographic situations in China and Mexico is that:
  a. population growth relates to other facets of societal life, e.g., political, religious, and familial beliefs;
  b. population growth has a very significant influence on the economy and lives of individuals;
  c. the populations of both countries will always rise faster than food production;
  *d. only a and b above;
  e. all of the above.

830. (p. 325) (LD)   The current U.S. population growth rate of about 1 percent per year clearly parallels that of:
  *a. Western Europe;
  b. Africa;
  c. Mexico;
  d. China;
  e. Latin America.

831. (p. 325) (MD)   Without a drop in the fertility rate, the number of births per year in the United States during the next two decades can be expected to:
  a. decrease significantly;
  b. increase moderately;
  c. decrease moderately;
  d. stay the same;
  *e. increase significantly.

832. (p. 325) (MD)   The primary factor which will contribute to population growth in the United States in the future is expected to be:
  *a. fecundity;
  b. birth rate;
  c. fertility;
  d. urbanization;
  e. mortality.

833. (p. 325) (LD) In the year 2000, the population of the United States, according to the text, is expected to be about:
   a. 200 million;
   b. 400 million;
   *c. 300 million;
   d. one billion;
   e. 500 million.

834. (pp. 326-327) (LD) Population growth in the United States during the post World War II period resulted in problems in which of the following areas of life?
   a. military service;
   b. food supply;
   c. crime and deviance;
   *d. education and jobs;
   e. all of the above.

835. (pp. 327-328) (LD) The comparison given in the textbook of white and nonwhite fertility rates showed that:
   a. the nonwhite rate is higher than the white rate;
   b. the nonwhite rate is going up;
   c. both the white and nonwhite rates are going down;
   d. only a and b;
   *e. only a and c.

836. (p. 330) (MD) Which of the following is true concerning current American practices of birth-control methods such as the pill?
   a. attitudes are becoming more and more favorable toward contraception;
   b. fertility regulation patterns for American women have been significantly changed in recent years;
   c. Catholics have been about as likely as Protestants to adopt the pill and to favor family planning;
   *d. all of the above;
   e. only a and b are true.

837. (p. 331) (MD) Significant reductions in birth rates in the so-called underdeveloped countries of Asia and Latin America will ultimately depend upon:
   a. the level of industrialization achieved;
   b. the availability of contraceptives;
   *c. popular attitudes toward fertility and family planning;
   d. economic aid from the U.S.;
   e. all of the above.

838. (p. 333) (LD) Concerning population control in Latin America, the text maintains that:
   a. it is unlikely that traditional beliefs concerning the importance of a large family will soon be abandoned;
   b. the ideal male role includes the expectation of virility, sexual activity, and fathering children;
   c. the influence of Catholicism regarding birth control has been strong;
   d. traditional patterns of religion, family, and government are in a state of change;
   *e. all of the above are true.

839. (p. 335) (LD) The very high birth rates in Muslim countries are
related to:
a. early marriages;
b. male dominance;
c. emphasis on sexual pleasure;
*d. all of the above;
e. only a and b above.

840. (p. 336) (MD) The authors conclude from their discussion of demographic change that the rate of world population growth must inevitably
decline. Which of the following factors can we reasonably expect will
contribute to this decline?
a. war, famine, and plague;
b. reduced birth rates;
c. increased death rates;
d. all of the above;
*e. only b and c.

True-False

841. (p. 304) (LD) The patterns and problems of population growth are
essentially the same throughout the world despite some societies that
lag behind others.
a. true;
*b. false.

842. (p. 306) (LD) Malthus advocated using certain "positive checks" to
keep the population down, such as wars, famines, etc.
a. true;
*b. false.

843. (p. 306) (MD) The theories of Malthus were so gloomy and improbable
to people of his time that his ideas had little or no influence on
his society.
a. true;
*b. false.

844. (p. 307) (LD) Prior to modern times (before 1800), birth rates were
generally even higher than they are now.
*a. true;
b. false.

845. (p. 307) (LD) As the statistical study of populations, demography
is concerned with such stable things as birth and death rates, but
not with migration and other matters of population mobility.
a. true;
*b. false.

846. (p. 308) (LD) Contrary to the dire predictions of Malthus, both
population and standard of living in the Western world have increased
since about 1800.
*a. true;
b. false.

847. (p. 310) (MD) The most important reason for the change in attitudes
regarding the conscious limitation of family size in industrialized

societies is the development of contraceptives.
a. true;
*b. false.

848. (p. 311) (MD) The consequences of the demographic transition for
population growth have <u>not</u> been the same in all societies.
*a. true;
b. false.

849. (p. 313) (LD) It was noted that urban growth in Latin America
differs from the urbanization of the rest of the Western world in
that it has not been stimulated by industrial and economic growth.
*a. true;
b. false.

850. (p. 313) (MD) A smaller percentage of the national wealth is drained
off by nonproductive consumers in developing countries than in
developed ones.
a. true;
*b. false.

851. (pp. 313-315) (LD) Developing countries have a large proportion of
consumers. This reduces the amount of money that can be put into
investment.
*a. true;
b. false.

852. (p. 316) (MD) As one of the leaders in industrialization among
developing nations of the world, Mexico is one of the few such
nations in which industrial and economic growth are keeping up with
population.
a. true;
*b. false.

853. (p. 313) (MD) One point made by the authors in comparing the history
of economic growth in various kinds of countries was that a decline
in birth rates was a <u>consequence</u> of economic growth in developed
countries, whereas in developing countries, a birth rate decline is
a necessary <u>prerequisite</u> to economic growth.
*a. true;
b. false.

854. (p. 317) (LD) As a result of sustained efforts since the revolution,
Mexico has largely succeeded in its goal of wiping out illiteracy.
a. true;
*b. false.

855. (p. 318) (LD) As is true of most industrializing countries, Mexico
is no longer very much influenced by traditional religious teachings
on birth control.
a. true;
*b. false.

856. (p. 322) (LD) In its national population policies since taking power,
the Communist regime in China has largely accepted the theory of
Malthus on population growth and has started a crash program of

population control.
a.   true;
*b. false.

857. (p. 322) (MD) The first "Five-Year Plan" in Communist China, though
      it had some setbacks, was generally quite successful in the realm of
      agriculture.
      a.   true;
      *b. false.

858. (pp. 322-323) (LD) Generally speaking, the Communist regime in
      China, since it took power more than twenty years ago, has followed
      a consistent policy on birth control and family planning.
      a.   true;
      *b. false.

859. (p. 325) (MD) One lesson of the cases of Mexico and China is that
      there is little hope for a reduction in the population crisis during
      the current decade.
      *a. true;
      b.   false.

860. (pp. 325-330) (MD) In their discussion of the population problem in
      the United States, the authors of the text suggest that it is not so
      much a problem of the kind Malthus warned about, but rather a problem
      relating to the quality of life.
      *a. true;
      b.   false.

861. (p. 327) (LD) Economic growth in the United States depends not so
      much on population growth as on the amount of disposable income.
      *a. true;
      b.   false.

862. (p. 310) (MD) A graph presented in the text comparing birth rates
      in developed and underdeveloped countries shows that the birth rate
      in underdeveloped countries remained the same from 1850 to 1950.
      *a. true;
      b.   false.

Fill-In

863. (p. 305) (LD) A theory based on the belief that people's biological
      drive for sexual gratification was essentially incompatible with
      their material needs was formulated by _____.

      Thomas Malthus

864. (p. 308) (LD) The situation in which high mortality rates and high
      fertility rates become low mortality rates and low fertility rates
      is called the _____ _____.

      demographic transition

865. (p. 315) (LD) The ejido system of farming in _____ works
      against modern agriculture progress.

      Mexico

866. (p. 313) (MD) In developing countries, a reduction of birth rates seems to be a _____ for economic and social progress.

prerequisite

867. (p. 323) (LD) _____ lacks good, reliable statistics on its population and economic growth.

China

868. (pp. 333-335) (MD) In Latin American countries, India, and the Muslim countries, the impact of _____ remains strong, making a significant drop in fertility rates unlikely.

tradition

Matching

869. (pp. 305-307) (LD)
Industrial Revolution

famine, plague, etc.
moral restraints
demography
job specialization

gradual reduction in death rates
"positive checks"
"preventative checks"
study of populations
lowered birth rates

870. (pp. 312-315) (MD)
lack of capital investments in developing countries
difference between developing countries and those already developed
increase in per capita income

helps account for continued high birth rates in developing countries
rapid population growth

large proportion of consumers

urban growth stimulated by economic growth

3 percent annual increase in investments
little social mobility

impedes modernization

871. (pp. 315-330) (LD)
1 percent population growth
development of good census bureau
ejido system
Five-Year Plan
goal to double production in one year

United States
Mexico

Mexico
China
China

872. (pp. 318-335) (MD)
government has announced support of family planning programs
gradually moving toward family planning programs
supports family planning program within the country and abroad
little knowledge of birth control except in the cities
birth control is in opposition to religion

Mexico

China

United States

Muslim countries

Latin countries

Short Essay

873. (pp. 305-307) (LD) Briefly explain the theory advanced by Thomas Malthus.

Major points: efforts to improve people's standard of living were destined to fail; populations would grow to the point where they could no longer be supported by the food supply; then through "positive checks" such as famines and diseases, the death rate would rise.

874. (pp. 307-309) (MD) Briefly describe the demographic transition that has taken place in the industrialized world.

Major points: movement from high mortality and fertility rates to low mortality and fertility rates; death rates dropped first, but birth rates gradually fell also; at present, the rates of growth in most industrialized nations seem to be stabilizing at relatively low levels.

875. (pp. 312-315) (MD) Explain the effect rapid population growth has on the labor force in developing countries.

Major points: it floods the labor market with workers; without a significant amount of capital available to invest in new productive facilities each year, a country will have increasing numbers of un- employed people; little economic progress will occur with this condition.

876. (p. 307) (LD) Define demography and discuss two of its concepts.

Major points: statistical study of population, size, distribution, and composition; concepts could be population growth rate, death rate, birth rate, fertility rate, or fecundity rate.

Broad Essay

877. (pp. 309-315) (LD) Discuss some of the demographic changes taking place in the developing countries.

Major points: revolution in mortality control; lack of reduction in births; traditionalism versus change.

878. (pp. 312-315) (MD) Explain why the decline of birth rates was a consequence of sociocultural changes that accompanied economic growth in industrialized nations and seems to be a prerequisite for economic growth in developing nations.

Major points: industrial societies: industrialization gradually changed the character of family life; it made families less self- sufficient and made children a family expense--this aided in chang- ing attitudes and traditions regarding family size, education, etc.; developing countries: there has been no concomitant change in atti- tudes and traditions regarding family size; with low death rates and high birth rates there are more people to provide education, health care, and housing for; this results in less capital for economic investment.

879. (pp. 317, 323, 330) (LD) Compare the current situations concerning birth control in Mexico, China, and the United States.

Major points: Mexico: the government has finally taken steps to introduce family planning; China: the government has gradually moved toward family planning programs, but demand for contraceptives is still light; U.S.: government has taken increasingly strong stand on family planning; large percentage of population supports family planning.

880. (pp. 325-330) (MD) Does the United States have a population problem? Explain.

Major points: the U.S. does have a population problem; this can be illustrated by showing the problems that have risen in the areas of education, jobs, and racial relations.

CHAPTER 12. The Urban Transition

Multiple Choice

881. (p. 338) (MD) Which of the following statements would be most correct about cities in history?
  *a. they have long been controversial;
   b. they have always been admired by intellectuals;
   c. pollution in cities was unknown prior to the automobile;
   d. they have long been regarded as centers of human virtue;
   e. all intellectuals have been antiurban for centuries.

882. (p. 338) (LD) The urbanization of people is essentially a phenomenon of:
   a. the twentieth century;
  *b. the last two centuries;
   c. the post World War II period;
   d. the last six thousand years;
   e. the last thousand years.

883. (p. 339) (LD) Preindustrial cities emerged mainly in areas of:
  *a. high soil fertility;
   b. good harbors;
   c. strong religious culture;
   d. flat land;
   e. powerful military leaders.

884. (p. 339) (MD) All of the following statements are true of the preindustrial cities, except which one?
   a. they were ruled ultimately by religion ("theocratic");
  *b. as centers of learning and progress, they had lower rates of death and disease than did the surrounding countryside;
   c. they had a rigid system of stratification;
   d. they served as agents of social change in the larger society;
   e. they developed only in areas of well-developed agriculture.

885. (p. 339) (LD) Political control in the earliest cities was typically:

a. polytheistic;
b. democratic;
*c. theocratic;
d. oligarchic;
e. monotheistic.

886. (p. 341) (LD) At present, what proportion of the U.S. population lives in places officially designated as <u>urban</u>?
a. approximately half;
b. about one fourth;
c. less than ten percent;
d. nearly ninety percent;
*e. about three fourths.

887. (p. 341) (LD) The major cause of urban growth in the U.S. and elsewhere has long been:
a. the higher birth rates in the city compared to lower rural rates;
b. the rapidly lowering death rate plus continued high birth rate in the city;
*c. the movement of rural people to the city;
d. migration into cities by persons of foreign origin;
e. all of the above have been major causes.

888. (p. 341) (MD) There has been much criticism of cities by American intellectuals. Such criticism is based on:
*a. a strong survival of the agrarian tradition in this country;
b. the fact that most American cities had low esteem for the arts;
c. the intense pollution found in early American cities;
d. the differential moral codes that developed in cities <u>vs.</u> rural areas;
e. the decline of religious values in the city.

889. (pp. 343-345) (MD) The major population trends in the United States during recent decades have included all of the following <u>except</u> which one?
a. East to West;
b. South to North;
*c. greater urban concentration and density;
d. rural to urban;
e. disproportionate migration of blacks from rural to urban and south to north.

890. (pp. 343-345) (LD) American urban centers have been influenced by which of the population trends indicated below?
a. East-to-West migrations;
b. South-to-North migrations;
c. central city to suburb migrations;
d. rural to urban movements;
*e. all of the above.

891. (p. 344) (LD) Which of the following accounts for the East-to-West migration?
a. increased immigration from Asia has moved the center of population gravity West;
b. opening of economic opportunities in the West;
c. inability of immigrants to acquire land in the East;

d.   immigration has been primarily from Europe;
*e.   b and d only.

892.   (p. 344) (MD)   The proportion of American blacks still living in the
       South at the present amounts to about what percent?
       a.   25 percent;
       b.   75 percent;
*c.   50 percent;
       d.   90 percent;
       e.   33 percent.

893.   (p. 347) (LD)   Which of the following statements is most correct
       concerning urbanization in the developing countries?
       a.   urbanization is actually declining in many so-called developing
             countries;
*b.   urbanization is proceeding more rapidly than it did in the
             United States;
       c.   urbanization is proceeding in developing countries but not as
             rapidly as it did in the U.S.;
       d.   rates of urbanization in developing countries are very similar
             to those in the U.S. during the last half of the nineteenth
             century;
       e.   urbanization has all but stopped in developing countries.

894.   (p. 347) (MD)   A major trend in Latin American countries concerning
       urbanization is:
*a.   the continued rapid growth of capital cities, resulting in severe
             centralization and poverty;
       b.   decentralization and the growth of middle-class suburbs (as in
             the U.S.);
       c.   a decline in the populations of capital cities but rapid growth
             in smaller towns;
       d.   the development all over the continent of modern new cities
             designed by master urban planners;
       e.   the decreasing urbanization in countries such as Argentina (more
             advanced) and increasing urbanization in such countries as
             Paraguay (less advanced).

895.   (pp. 347-348) (MD)   Areas such as the favelas of Rio de Janeiro:
*a.   provide conditions barely capable of sustaining human life;
       b.   serve as models for cities wanting to provide sanitary living
             conditions for the poor;
       c.   are unparalleled in their concentration of wealth, talent, and
             cultural advantage;
       d.   are examples of what a successful urban renewal program can be
             like;
       e.   are often referred to by sociologists as the ideal solution
             concerning urban housing for the elderly.

896.   (p. 347) (LD)   Which of the following is an accurate comparison of
       urbanization in developing and industrial societies?
       a.   the family is still important in urban areas of developing
             societies whereas it is not important in urban areas of industrial
             societies;
       b.   religion is a central activity in urban areas of both types of
             societies;

    *c. the central city in developing societies is occupied by middle
        and upper classes, while it is occupied by lower classes in
        industrial societies;
    d. all of the above;
    e. none of the above.

897. (p. 347) (MD) According to theorists of urban life, the focus of
     interaction in the city has moved away from the family and centered
     increasingly around:
    a. manufacturing and service industries;
    b. organized sports and other recreation;
    c. religious and ethnic institutions;
   *d. economic and governmental organizations;
    e. peer groups and associations.

898. (p. 349) (MD) The text defined <u>urbanism</u> as:
    a. the force that pulls people from farmlands to towns and cities;
   *b. patterns of social organization and culture that characterize
       city life;
    c. something that only occurs in industrialized societies;
    d. the process of becoming urbane and cultured;
    e. a theory of urban life.

899. (p. 349) (LD) A small society has a number of the following char-
     acteristics: preliteracy, homogeneity, high solidarity, simple
     technology, and division of labor. Robert Redfield would probably
     classify such a society as a:
   *a. folk society;
    b. primitive society;
    c. savage society;
    d. simple society;
    e. preurban society.

900. (p. 349) (MD) In the "folk society" as elaborated conceptually by
     Redfield, the central unit of action is the:
    a. peer group;
   *b. family;
    c. church;
    d. association;
    e. age stratum.

901. (p. 350) (LD) According to Louis Wirth in "Urbanism as a Way of
     Life," urban life is characterized by:
    a. heterogeneity;
    b. tolerance of differences;
    c. decline in kinship ties;
    d. impersonality;
   *e. all of the above.

902. (p. 350) (LD) Sociologists have proposed the idea that natural
     forces operate in human communities, as they do in plant and animal
     communities, to clearly differentiate certain social activities
     into defined spatial areas. This view is called the:
    a. spatial theory;
    b. land-use configuration;
    c. succession-invasion hypothesis;

*d.   ecological approach;
 e.   zonal specialization concept.

903.   (pp. 351-353) (LD)   Attempts to describe the spatial structuring of cities have led to which of the following "ecological models"?
  a.   concentric zone theory;
  b.   sector theory;
  c.   multiple nuclei theory;
*d.   all of the above;
 e.   a and b above.

904.   (p. 351) (MD)   Attempts to apply the concentric zone model to a study of city life have indicated that the model fits which of the following kinds of cities?
  a.   the earliest preindustrial cities;
*b.   the cities which grew during the period of heavy immigration;
  c.   the cities that have grown since the advent of the automobile;
  d.   all of the above;
 e.   only b and c.

905.   (pp. 353-354) (MD)   Louis Wirth's theories concerning the nature of city life have been criticized by contemporary sociologists such as Gans. These criticisms point out that:
*a.   Wirth based his explanation of urbanism upon the wrong variables;
 b.   economic factors are actually responsible for the increasing anonymity of the city;
 c.   there is really very little difference between the way of life in an urban center and in a small town;
 d.   only transients and the foreign-born have the characteristics suggested by Wirth's theories;
 e.   all of the above are true.

906.   (p. 355) (LD)   The factor contributing most to keeping some dwellers "trapped" in deteriorating sections of the city, according to the text, is:
*a.   poverty;
 b.   urban renewal;
 c.   politics;
 d.   racial discrimination;
 e.   different value system.

907.   (pp. 358-359) (MD)   Urban renewal programs appear for the most part to benefit:
  a.   the nonwhite;
*b.   middle and upper classes;
 c.   ethnic (but not racial) minorities;
 d.   families with numerous children;
 e.   recent migrants to the city.

908.   (p. 359) (LD)   The principal factor contributing to the "growing crisis of the cities" in the United States is:
  a.   cultural diversity;
  b.   social disorganization;
*c.   racial discrimination;
 d.   creeping socialism;
 e.   urban renewal.

909. (p. 362) (MD) Suburbs are:
    a. a phenomenon of the twentieth century;
    b. the source from which the central city gets most of its tax
        returns;
   *c. decreasing in density;
    d. starting to level off in terms of population movement from the
        city to suburbs;
    e. none of the above.

910. (pp. 361-362) (LD) What is new about suburbs in recent times is
that:
    a. they attract residents at a very rapid rate;
    b. the vast majority of residents are white;
    c. they extract more wealth from the city than they return to it;
    d. they are decreasing in density;
   *e. all of the above are true.

911. (p. 362) (LD) Research has shown that the life-style in the suburbs
(as contrasted with the central city) is characterized by:
    a. more primary interaction;
    b. greater ethnic homogeneity;
    c. more satisfying family life;
    d. cultural richness;
   *e. occupational and educational homogeneity.

912. (p. 364) (MD) Research on the urban family reveals that:
    a. there is almost no interaction in the city along kinship lines;
   *b. kinship ties remain relatively strong, contrary to the classic
        theories of family life in urban-industrial society;
    c. kinship ties remain strong only among recent migrants to the city;
    d. the poor retain strong kinship ties in the city but the middle
        class do not;
    e. middle-class people retain kinship ties in the city, but poor
        families break down and become disorganized.

913. (p. 367) (LD) The text maintains that "urban life has become
bureaucratically organized." This means:
    a. the primary group has declined in significance for urban people;
   *b. the overwhelming majority of employed Americans work for some
        type of bureaucratic organization;
    c. life in the city is impersonal, anonymous, and regimented, much
        as in a bureaucratic organization;
    d. the functions performed by the family in rural and suburban
        areas are performed by bureaucracies in the central city;
    e. both a and d are correct.

914. (p. 367) (MD) Research on extent of participation in voluntary
organizations shows that such participation correlates positively
with which of the following factors?
    a. occupational prestige;
    b. income;
    c. education;
   *d. all of the above;
    e. only b and c.

915. (p. 370) (LD) The study of Springdale revealed that small-town folk
have a clear conception of what life is like in the city. Perhaps
the best description of their view is that:
   a. they envied city people and the richness of their cultural
opportunities;
   b. they approved of most aspects of city life but disliked some
features intensely;
*c. they pitied the city people living in a jostling and nerve-
racking environment;
   d. they saw the city as financially attractive but socially dull;
   e. they disapproved mainly of the lack of religious convictions of
most city people.

916. (p. 371) (MD) The text takes a position concerning the role of
small-town people with respect to urban problems. Essentially, the
authors conclude:
   a. small-town people play no part in creating urban problems, but
share a moral responsibility for helping solve them;
   b. small-town people have played a part in helping create urban
problems, but have no responsibility for aiding in their solution;
*c. small-town people share responsibility for creating and solving
urban problems;
   d. small-town people have no relationship to urban problems one
way or the other;
   e. basically, urban problems have been caused primarily by small-
town people who have moved to the city.

917. (p. 342) (MD) A town in the United States might be designated as
urban by the Census Bureau with a population as small as:
   a. 5000;
   b. 10,000
   c. 20,000;
   d. 50,000;
*e. 2500.

True-False

918. (p. 339) (LD) Urban life is ultimately dependent on the existence of
food surpluses.
*a. true;
   b. false.

919. (p. 339) (LD) Whatever the "cut-off" point is in deciding how small
a town might be considered urban, the essential point is that its
economic activities should be predominantly nonagricultural.
*a. true;
   b. false.

920. (p. 341) (MD) In spite of the overwhelming urbanization in the
United States, agricultural traditions remain strong in this country.
*a. true;
   b. false.

921. (p. 344) (MD) At the present time, the chief source of growth for the
black population of the big cities is births rather than in-migration.

*a. true;
b. false.

922. (p. 345) (LD) According to the 1970 census, more Americans live in the suburbs than in the big cities.
*a. true;
b. false.

923. (p. 345) (MD) The urbanization of the United States is by now so complete that it is difficult to make valid and significant distinctions between urban and rural life.
*a. true;
b. false.

924. (p. 348) (LD) Sociologists have developed an interest in urban studies only since World War I, because prior to that time most societies were agrarian in nature.
a. true;
*b. false.

925. (p. 349) (LD) The ideal concept of the "folk society" implies a condition of social stability with very little change over time.
*a. true;
b. false.

926. (p. 349) (MD) One generalization in Wirth's ideal concept of the nature of urban life was that, as the number of people in social interaction increases, the intensity of the interaction decreases.
*a. true;
b. false.

927. (p. 350) (LD) The ecological theorists of urban life have argued that certain natural forces operate in human communities, just as they do in animal and plant communities.
*a. true;
b. false.

928. (pp. 353-354) (LD) It would appear from the textbook's treatment of Wirth's ideas on "urbanism as a way of life" that sociologists are all pretty well in agreement with those ideas.
a. true;
*b. false.

929. (p. 354) (MD) The well-known study of slums, Street-Corner Society, found that social life in the slums was generally characterized by large-scale social disorganization and ambiguous value systems.
a. true;
*b. false.

930. (p. 359) (LD) Urban renewal programs have given precedence to the interests of the more affluent people over the interests of the poor.
*a. true;
b. false.

931. (p. 361) (MD) In discussing "the growth crisis of the cities," the textbook indicates that there is something inherent in urban life

that tends to produce alienation and discontent.
a. true;
*b. false.

932. (p. 361) (LD) Due to the efforts of the civil rights movement and legislation in recent years, the gap in income and education is clearly closing between the inner city and the outer city or suburbs.
a. true;
*b. false.

933. (p. 362) (LD) The growth of suburbs in the United States has been determined more by the factor of travel time than of travel distance itself.
*a. true;
b. false.

934. (p. 363) (LD) Current statistics reported in the text indicate that the trend of movement to the suburbs is slowing down and may shortly come almost to an end.
a. true;
*b. false.

935. (p. 362) (LD) Sociologists at present are not sure whether suburban social life differs at all from city life in any important respects.
*a. true;
b. false.

936. (p. 362) (MD) The most recent research on suburbs indicates that city-suburban differences in life-style are primarily the product of underlying differences in class.
*a. true;
b. false.

937. (p. 364) (MD) Recent studies on family life in urban areas indicate that love, affection, and other Gemeinschaft-like qualities are disappearing from family relationships in the cities.
a. true;
*b. false.

938. (p. 367) (LD) One of the reasons that many sociologists have expressed concern about the growing bureaucratic trends in our society is that bureaucracies tend to destroy warm primary relationships among people.
a. true;
*b. false.

939. (p. 367) (MD) Recent evidence on minority group participation in voluntary associations suggests that for blacks such participation is greater than for Mexican-Americans.
a. true;
*b. false.

940. (p. 365) (MD) An example of a simple random design for a sample would be to include in the sample every tenth person standing in a cafeteria line.
a. true;
*b. false.

Fill-In

941. (p. 339) (LD) The _____ city was characterized by theocratic
control, a rigid social stratification system, and the limitation of
education to the wealthy.

preindustrial

942. (p. 341) (LD) _____ is the process whereby a population
moves from farmlands to towns and cities.

Urbanization

943. (p. 345) (MD) The most significant movement now being made is not
between rural and urban but rather between _____ and

_____.

city and suburbs

944. (p. 349) (LD) Redfield's _____ _____ was characterized as small, isolated, and culturally and physically homogeneous.

folk society

945. (p. 367) (MD) Evidence seems to suggest that _____
_____ have not taken the place of primary groups, but rather
supplement them.

voluntary associations

946. (p. 342) (MD) A _____ is a county or group of contiguous
counties which contains at least one city of 50,000 inhabitants or
more or "twin cities" with a combined population of at least 50,000.

SMSA (Standard Metropolitan Statistical Area)

Matching

947. (pp. 341-345) (MD)
city--suburbs   most significant population
                                           shift today
rural--urban   hard to make significant dis-
                                           tinctions between the two
North--South   white collar and professionals
South--North   uneducated and unskilled
East--West   stimulated by immigration

948. (pp. 349-362) (LD)
ideal type   folk society
competition for land   ecological approach
decreasing density   suburb
lack residential choice   "deprived"
urban renewal   aids middle and upper class

949. (pp. 355-367) (LD)
decreasing density   suburbs
core city dwellers   deprived and trapped
urban renewal   benefit wealthy

crisis of cities   racial discrimination
urbanite   bureaucracy

950. (p. 365) (MD)
      list of all population members   sampling frame
      accurately reflects population   representative sample
        characteristics
      probabilities of selection equal   simple random design
      spatial sampling units   area sample
      most complex   multistage sample

Short Essay

951. (pp. 341-345) (MD) It was noted that the rural-urban population
      shift is nearing completion. Name the most significant population
      shift occurring today and explain why it is so important.

      Major points: shift is from city to suburbs; it's important because
      it is the poor who stay in the cities and the middle- and upper-class
      people who are moving out; this shift has been accelerating rapidly
      and has been increasingly tied to patterns of racial segregation.

952. (pp. 349-350) (LD) Briefly describe Robert Redfield's "folk society"
      and tell how it was considered important in understanding urban life.

      Major points: it was an ideal type; small, isolated, preliterate,
      and homogeneous; kinship is central to the society and status is
      fixed at birth; communication is face to face; it was felt that much
      could be learned about the modern urban community by contrasting it
      with the folk society.

953. (p. 355) (LD) Herbert Gans identified five different types of inner-
      city residents. Name and briefly discuss each type.

      Major points: 1. cosmopolites--intellectuals and professionals;
      2. unmarried or childless--generally middle class in orientation;
      3. ethnic villagers--2nd and 3rd generation Europeans; 4. deprived--
      very poor and nonwhite; 5. trapped--those that stay in a neighborhood
      invaded by nonresidential land use, etc., because they can't afford
      to move out.

954. (pp. 367-368) (MD) Briefly discuss the role of voluntary associations
      in American urban life.

      Major points: majority of people are members of voluntary associa-
      tions; may provide the means by which one can take part in shaping
      community life; evidence suggests that social class does not neces-
      sarily correlate negatively with membership; it was also suggested
      that voluntary organizations have not taken the place of primary
      groups, just supplement them.

Broad Essay

955. (pp. 339-341) (LD) Discuss how modern industrial cities differ from
      preindustrial cities and what changes have taken place in social
      organization.

      Major points: industrial cities have more fluid stratification
      system, and more activities that revolve around bureaucratic organiza-

tion; groups and individuals are increasingly interdependent; spatial patterns have also changed, with central area being relegated to the poor; the wealthy have moved to the outskirts; the economic and political institutions have become dominant, while the sphere of religion has narrowed.

956. (pp. 341-345) (MD) Urban growth in the United States has resulted from a large movement of people to urban centers. Name and discuss the five population shifts that have occurred and explain how these have contributed to some of our social problems today.

Major points: movements: East to West (rapid population shifts, decline of cities in some areas); North to South (exodus of blacks from urban ghettos); rural to urban (loss of rural and small-town population); city to suburbs (loss of tax revenues, concentration of low-income people and ghettos in central city).

957. (pp. 350-354) (MD) Identify and discuss the three major theories of urban growth that utilize the ecological approach. What particular criticisms has this approach faced?

Major points: three theories are: 1. concentric zone theory; 2. sector theory; 3. multiple nuclei theory; the urban organization of people cannot be accounted for simply by competitive economic processes; behavior cannot be explained in terms of just size, density, and heterogeneity; cultural factors are important.

958. (pp. 361-368) (LD) The shift away from the city to the suburbs is quite important in our society. Discuss the characteristics that set the suburbs off from the city. Describe the differences (if any) in life-styles between the two.

Major points: characteristics: suburbs are outside political boundaries of the city and they are residential areas of low density; evidence suggests that life-styles are not different because of living in the city or the suburb; rather the difference lies in neighbors based upon occupations and education; differences in life-styles seem to be the product of underlying differences in class, ethnicity, and family status.

CHAPTER 13. Corrective Behavior and Social Movement

Multiple Choice

959. (p. 374) (LD) Collective behavior, as defined in the text, is characteristically:
a. distinct from group behavior;
b. largely unpredictable;
c. unstructured;
d. lacking established norms;
*e. all of the above.

960. (p. 375) (MD) Sociologists are interested in the study of collective behavior principally because:

a. no other discipline seems to be interested;
b. it provides some of the clearest examples of institutionalized social systems;
*c. it often serves as a stimulant to sociocultural change;
d. it preserves existing sociocultural arrangements;
e. it aids the most deprived sectors of society.

961. (p. 377) (LD) Of the various kinds of crowds, the one characterized by the most intense emotion is called:
a. the angry crowd;
b. the charged crowd;
*c. the expressive crowd;
d. the casual crowd;
e. the intense crowd.

962. (p. 376) (LD) The least structured (in components of social organization) of all crowd forms discussed in the text is the:
a. incidental crowd;
b. disorganized crowd;
c. inactive crowd;
*d. casual crowd;
e. random crowd.

963. (p. 376) (MD) The people have all entered the movie theater and the film is about to begin. Such an assembly of persons would be classified by a student of collective behavior as a:
*a. conventional crowd;
b. theater group;
c. recreational crowd;
d. institutionalized category;
e. active aggregate.

964. (p. 376) (MD) The kind of crowd which comes closest to being an organized group is:
a. the organized crowd;
b. the expressive crowd;
c. the casual crowd;
*d. the conventionalized crowd;
e. the active crowd.

965. (pp. 376-377) (MD) A key characteristic which (according to Herbert Blumer's theories) clearly distinguishes an expressive crowd from an active crowd is which of the following?
a. the expressive crowd is religious in nature while the active crowd is essentially political;
*b. the expressive crowd lacks common goals or objectives; tensions are released individually in emotional behavior;
c. emotional contagion and suggestibility are more prominent in the active crowd;
d. the expressive crowd is characterized by social organization while the active crowd is rather unstructured;
e. all of the above.

966. (p. 377) (LD) The first systematic analysis of the social psychology of crowd behavior was presented by:

    a. Herbert Blumer;
*b. Gustav Le Bon;
    c. Émile Durkheim;
    d. Armand Mauss;
    e. Hadley Cantril.

967. (p. 380) (MD) The principal concepts in Le Bon's analysis of the
      social-psychological impact of the crowd on its members include all
      except which of the following?
*a. common norms;
    b. anonymity;
    c. contagion;
    d. reciprocal influence;
    e. unconscious motivation.

968. (p. 380) (LD) Inadequacies of norms (or other aspects of social
      structure) that play a part in generating collective behavior include
      which of the following?
    a. intercultural conflicts;
    b. discontinuities within a culture;
    c. conflicts in various elements of social organization;
*d. insufficient preparation of group members to handle crisis
        situations;
    e. all of the above.

969. (pp. 380-381) (LD) The four standard characteristics making up the
      dynamics of collective behavior include all except which one of the
      following?
*a. social organization gradually begins to set in;
    b. conventional norms become ineffective;
    c. emotional forms of behavior replace more rational forms;
    d. rumor helps make for new interpretations and for suggestibility;
    e. nonrational behavior diffuses throughout the crowd.

970. (pp. 380-384) (MD) The social dynamics of collective behavior can
      be summarized by all of the following necessary and sufficient condi-
      tions except which one?
    a. inadequate social organization;
    b. reciprocal generation of emotional orientations;
    c. the spread of common interpretive rumors;
*d. collective anger;
    e. epidemic-like diffusions of overt behavior.

971. (p. 380) (LD) The spread of emotional orientations from person to
      person in crowd situations is termed:
*a. emotional contagion;
    b. orientation spread;
    c. reciprocal transmission;
    d. mood similarity;
    e. interpersonal suggestibility.

972. (p. 381) (MD) In a group close to panic, member A appears frightened;
      this scares member B; this in turn heightens A's fears to a point
      where A screams; this causes B to run blindly. Such a set of inter-
      actions is called:

a. interpersonal provocation;
b. intermember reinforcement;
c. superorganic manipulation;
d. collective transmission;
*e. reciprocal stimulation.

973. (p. 382) (MD) A person is under the influence of strong religious
emotions at a prayer meeting. Suddenly, there is a minor earth
tremor; this is "seen" as the hand of a Divine Being giving a message
to sinners. This situation provides an illustration of:
a. focused attention;
*b. selective perception;
c. reciprocal innovation;
d. emotional homogeneity;
e. symbolic intervention.

974. (p. 383) (MD) The various kinds of content distortion that occur
in serial retelling of messages (in the experimental study of rumor)
are called the:
*a. embedding pattern;
b. serial distortion phenomenon;
c. interpersonal transmission effect;
d. reality alteration result;
e. content reduction coefficient.

975. (p. 383) (LD) As a rumor travels, it tends to grow shorter, more
concise, more easily grasped and told. Sociologically, this is
referred to as:
a. shortening;
b. cutting;
c. simplification;
d. summarization;
*e. leveling.

976. (p. 383) (MD) The so-called embedding pattern of rumor spreading has
generally been studied by which of the following methods?
a. large-scale sample surveys;
*b. experimental studies;
c. participant observation;
d. sociometric studies;
e. field experiments.

977. (p. 384) (MD) As rumors are retold (in laboratory studies) they
tend to become fused with a combination of common cultural themes,
plus the attitudinal and interest biases of the subjects who actually
do the retelling. This phenomenon is called:
a. fusion;
b. configuration;
c. amalgamation;
d. compounding;
*e. assimilation.

978. (p. 384) (LD) The text cites a field study of the diffusion of a
rumor in a small community, concerning the murder of a babysitter.
Elaborate accounts of the activities, motivations, and characteristics of Mr. X (who was supposed to have done it) were circulated.

The incident illustrates the:
a. embedding pattern;
b. confusion pattern;
c. amalgamation pattern;
d. fusion pattern;
*e. compounding pattern.

979. (p. 384) (LD) According to the textbook, rumors:
a. can always be traced back to an authentic source;
b. are seldom accepted at face value by the population in which they spread;
*c. are one of the more significant processes underlying the process of collective behavior;
d. are more a product of reflective rationality than ambiguity and stress;
e. are characterized by all of the above.

980. (p. 385) (LD) In a collective behavior situation, an "innovator" suddenly commits an overt act (such as throwing a rock at a police car). Others see this as an "apparent norm" and do the same. We have here an instance of:
a. collective delusion;
b. interpersonal symbolism;
c. instinctual imitation;
*d. behavioral diffusion;
e. role transmission.

981. (pp. 385-390) (MD) From a sociological point of view, urban ghetto upheavals such as the Watts riot can best be understood as:
a. communist-inspired attempts to disrupt the functioning of American cities;
b. results of deliberate attempts to start trouble by the delinquent and gangster element in ghettos;
c. caused by black militant groups according to a master plan;
d. an inevitable result of giving blacks too much freedom too soon;
*e. incidents of collective behavior that expand step-by-step into large-scale civil disorders.

982. (p. 385) (MD) Chronic societal discontinuities (e.g., discriminatory societal norms in a "democratic" society) represent flaws in the social structure. These play a part in the etiology of riots. That is, they:
a. are not truly necessary but serve as sufficient preconditions;
b. are causal factors in their own right, triggering violent upheavals;
*c. are necessary but not sufficient preconditions;
d. are somewhat indirectly related to the outbreak of riots;
e. are themselves the result rather than the cause of riots.

983. (pp. 385-391) (LD) Which of the following is a truly significant factor in the "anatomy of a riot"?
a. inadequacies in the social structure;
b. the spread of generalized beliefs;
c. a precipitating incident;
d. the effects of emotional and behavioral contagion;
*e. all of the above.

984. (p. 386) (MD) The case study of the Leeville Lynching has theoretical significance in that:
   a. the social dynamics of this instance of collective behavior differed greatly from those of the Watts riot;
   b. the black population in this case burned fewer buildings than in Watts;
   c. it shows lynching to be the result of deliberate plans of prejudiced people;
   *d. it paralleled the Watts situation to some extent, indicating that sociological factors shape collective action in spite of specific differences;
   e. it calls into question the whole theory of collective behavior encompassed in the analysis of the Watts riot.

985. (pp. 387-388) (MD) According to the text, the most relevant generalized belief prior to the riot in Watts was:
   a. white racism;
   b. widespread poverty;
   c. political corruption;
   d. the innocence of an arrested black youth;
   *e. police brutality.

986. (pp. 387-388) (LD) Before the Watts riot, an important factor contributing to the generalized belief in police brutality was:
   a. the overwhelming number of well-documented cases of police abuse of innocent blacks;
   *b. the fact that the police were visible agents of the dominating white establishment;
   c. the fact that the police were so portrayed by mass media of Los Angeles;
   d. the fact that police had official orders to give blacks brutal treatment;
   e. the recent campaign on the part of the police to get tough with black militants.

987. (p. 388) (LD) A major factor in setting the stage for the Watts riot that contributed greatly to the mobilization of potential actors was:
   *a. the hot humid weather;
   b. street-corner agitators;
   c. black militants on corners;
   d. the recent black-white gang fights;
   e. the electrical blackout that evening.

988. (p. 390) (MD) In the Watts riot, as described in the textbook, the young man under arrest did not begin to resist the police until:
   a. they clubbed him;
   b. his pregnant wife started to scream;
   c. the crowd began to encourage him;
   *d. his mother berated him;
   e. a barber started shouting insults at the police.

989. (p. 391) (MD) In the Watts riot, the "recruitment of additional participants," after the riot was touched off, resulted mainly from which of the following factors?

*a. the spread of rumors about the original incident;
 b. the effective resistance of the police to the initial rioters;
 c. the prompt arrival of the National Guard;
 d. the widespread burning of buildings;
 e. all of the above.

990. (p. 392) (LD) The precipitating circumstances of the 1965 Watts riot involved all of the following except which one?
 a. suspect arrested for drunken driving;
 b. suspect's mother's reaction;
*c. sudden arrival of National Guard;
 d. clubbing of suspect by police;
 e. abuse of police by young female bystander.

991. (p. 394) (LD) Concerning the occurrence of riots in the United States, it can be said confidently that:
 a. there were no riots of consequence in the U.S. prior to World War II;
 b. only since 1960 have Americans witnessed true riots in their own country;
 c. riots occur mainly during wartime, such as the Civil War and World War II;
*d. we have had riots at various times and places throughout our nation's history;
 e. American experience with riots shows them to be on the decline in recent decades.

992. (p. 394) (LD) Relatively organized collective activity aimed at changing existing social arrangements is called:
 a. collective behavior;
*b. a social movement;
 c. a riot;
 d. organized crowd;
 e. rumor.

993. (p. 394) (LD) Which of the following characteristics is not common to all social movements?
 a. shared orientations (values, attitudes);
 b. sense of shared identity;
*c. loose social organization;
 d. shared norms and role definitions;
 e. all the above characteristics pertain to social movements.

994. (p. 396) (LD) Turner and Killian identify various types of social movements which include all of the following except:
 a. participation-oriented movements;
 b. power-oriented movements;
*c. action-oriented movements;
 d. value-oriented movements;
 e. all of the above have been identified by Turner and Killian.

995. (p. 396) (MD) Which of the following movements is the best example of Turner and Killian's "participation-oriented movement"?
 a. the women's movement;
 b. Nazism;
 c. population movement;

    d. Russian Bolshevism;
*e. the American Indian Ghost Dance cult.

996. (p. 402) (LD) The authors of the textbook conclude from their discussion of the women's movement in the United States that:
    a. there has not been a movement toward the equalization of pay for females and males;
    b. equalization of educational opportunities for males and females is not taking place;
    c. sex differences are no longer used in ranking people;
   *d. traditional patterns of sex ranking will not entirely disappear;
    e. a, b, and d are true.

True-False

997. (p. 374) (MD) One important characteristic distinguishing collective behavior from group behavior is the absence of social organization in all forms of collective behavior.
    a. true;
   *b. false.

998. (p. 377) (LD) Once a crowd forges itself into one of the major crowd types, it cannot be transformed into a different type without being totally destroyed and rebuilt.
    a. true;
   *b. false.

999. (p. 377) (MD) One of the key insights of Le Bon in his studies of crowds was that "crowd psychology" or the "collective mind" cannot overcome the inhibitions that society has built into the personality of an individual.
    a. true;
   *b. false.

1000. (p. 380) (MD) From a study of various crisis situations (such as sinkings, bombing, etc.), it appears that even advance training and preparation of the populace can do little or nothing to prevent disorganization and chaos once a real crisis gets going.
    a. true;
   *b. false.

1001. (p. 381) (LD) The most general and important effect of emotional contagion in crowd situations is to neutralize the norms and other restraints by which the behavior of the people is usually controlled.
   *a. true;
    b. false.

1002. (p. 381) (MD) One of the factors that contributes to the spread of emotional contagion in a crowd is a great diversification of moods, which has a social disorganizing effect on the crowd.
    a. true;
   *b. false.

1003. (p. 381) (LD) A crowd is more likely to become carried away with emotion if the members are similar to each other than if they are different.

*a. true;
 b. false.

1004. (p. 381) (MD) When the attention of individuals in a crowd is
      focused on a variety of different things, the crowd is disorganized,
      and emotional contagion is likely to spread.
       a. true;
      *b. false.

1005. (p. 381) (LD) One of the factors making emotional contagion more
      likely to spread is the anonymity which people often feel when they
      are in a large crowd.
      *a. true;
       b. false.

1006. (p. 381) (LD) One of the elements contributing to the spread of
      emotional contagion is "reciprocal stimulation," which refers to
      the pushing action characteristic of crowds.
       a. true;
      *b. false.

1007. (p. 382) (LD) The incidents of the mad gasser and the invasion from
      Mars illustrate that people respond to social constructions of
      reality and not to facts, per se.
      *a. true;
       b. false.

1008. (p. 383) (LD) As rumor spreads, there is selective perception,
      retention, and reporting of a limited number of details from a
      larger context.
      *a. true;
       b. false.

1009. (p. 383) (LD) The content of rumor, as it spreads, tends to become
      distorted in the direction of established habits, customs, and con-
      ventions.
      *a. true;
       b. false.

1010. (p. 384) (MD) The basic principle behind the so-called compounding
      pattern in the spread of rumor is that one rumor often simply
      demands another.
      *a. true;
       b. false.

1011. (pp. 384-385) (MD) According to the ideas of social psychologists
      presented in the textbook (Lang and Lang), behavioral contagion
      involves the processes of imitation and learning.
      *a. true;
       b. false.

1012. (p. 385) (MD) A key feature of "behavioral contagion" in crowd
      situations is that, in the absence of traditional and institutional-
      ized norms, innovative behavior seems to be normative.
      *a. true;
       b. false.

1013. (pp. 385-387) (MD) According to the textbook's treatment of the Watts riot, the conditions of the blacks in Watts prior to the riot were unusually bad, even for a congested urban area.
a.   true;
*b.   false.

1014. (p. 388) (LD) After investigation, it became clear that the young black man stopped by the police for drunken driving just prior to the Watts riot was stopped without good reason.
a.   true;
*b.   false.

1015. (p. 391) (LD) When the police began to withdraw from the immediate riot area as the Watts riot picked up momentum, a gradual calming began to occur because people believed that the police were leaving.
a.   true;
*b.   false.

1016. (p. 392) (MD) Studies of the Watts riot of 1965 showed that those arrested in the riot did not represent any unusual concentration of criminals, school dropouts, or juvenile delinquents.
*a.   true;
b.   false.

1017. (p. 392) (MD) During the 1965 Watts riot, a generalized pattern of retaliation against all whites could be seen not only in Watts itself, but also in other sections of the city as the rioting spread.
a.   true;
*b.   false.

1018. (p. 393) (LD) At the time it occurred, the Watts riot was the worst civil disorder ever to take place in the United States.
*a.   true;
b.   false.

1019. (p. 394) (LD) As severe as the Watts riot was, it had no more impact on the nation as a whole than had any of the earlier race riots.
*a.   true;
b.   false.

1020. (p. 396) (MD) Since the study of social movements is a recent phenomenon, typologies of social movements are only now being developed.
a.   true;
*b.   false.

1021. (p. 396) (LD) In the textbook, the Ghost Dance religion of 1890 was used as an example of collective behavior which developed to cope with severe conflict between Indians and whites.
*a.   true;
b.   false.

1022. (p. 396) (MD) According to the authors of your textbook the women's movement will never be entirely successful in eradicating sex ranking.

*a. true;
 b. false.

Fill-In

1023. (p. 376) (LD) The _____ crowd usually imposes simple
       norms and roles upon its members. Behavior, in effect, is ex-
       pressed in established and expected ways.

       conventionalized

1024. (p. 377) (MD) According to Blumer, members of a (an) _____
       crowd engage in mutual and reciprocal stimulation.

       expressive

1025. (p. 382) (MD) When people respond to a situation collectively, the
       factual accuracy of their shared interpretation is irrelevant:
       people respond not to facts per se but rather to their _____

       _____ _____ .

       social construction of reality

1026. (p. 382) (LD) An unverified report that is passed along from person
       to person is defined as a _____ .

       rumor

1027. (p. 383) (LD) Leveling, sharpening, and assimilation are key
       elements in the _____ pattern of rumor distortion.

       embedding

1028. (p. 394) (LD) A more-or-less organized collective activity aimed
       at correcting some perceived inadequacy in existing social arrange-
       ments is a _____ _____ .

       social movement

Matching

1029. (pp. 375–377) (LD)
       casual crowd   least structured of all
                                              collectivities
       conventionalized crowd   behavior is expressed in
                                              established ways
       expressive crowd   subjective feelings are
                                              principal feature
       conventionalized crowd   imposes simple norms and roles
       active crowd   engages in volatile forms of
                                              behavior

1030. (pp. 380–381) (MD)
       reduces the necessity for   anonymity
          constant self-monitoring
       distracts individual from   focused attention
          contemplation of rational
          alternatives
       leads to adoption of the   suggestibility
          emotional states of others

can raise emotional levels
  sharply and quickly

reciprocal stimulation

makes people more available to
  each other as role models

homogeneity of members

1031. (pp. 382-384) (MD)

threatening situations

compounding patterns

nonthreatening situations

embedding patterns

leveling

rumor grows shorter

sharpening

selective perception limits
  details

assimilation

distorts in accordance with
  cultural themes, attitudes,
  etc.

1032. (pp. 385-393) (LD)

inadequacies in the social
  structure

Watts was characterized by
  official apathy and neglect

generalized belief

police brutality in Watts

precipitating incident

suspect arrested for drunken
  driving

direct result of Watts riot

specific forms of social
  change

selective perception was key

manhandling by police of a
  pregnant woman

Short Essay

1033. (pp. 375-377) (LD) Describe the characteristics of the four types of crowds identified by Blumer.

Major points: casual: least structured in that it lacks any form of organization; conventionalized: behavior is expressed in established ways; active: openly engages in behavior directed toward persons, events, etc.; expressive: subjective experiences of the members are the principal feature of attention.

1034. (p. 377) (MD) Describe what Gustave LeBon, in his analysis of the crowd, meant by the "collective mind."

Major points: crowd can produce profound changes in the psychological functioning of its members.

1035. (pp. 380-385) (LD) Name and briefly describe the four processes that seem to be involved in the dynamics of collective behavior.

Major points: inadequacies of existing structures, emotional contagion, rumor, behavioral contagion.

1036. (pp. 394-397) (MD) Define social movements, give their major characteristics, and describe their stages of development.

Major points: social movements are more-or-less organized collective activities aimed at correcting some perceived inadequacy in existing social arrangements; they have in common shared orientations of their members, a sense of shared identity, and elements of social organization; movements frequently go through the following stages-- incipient, period of popular excitement, coalescence, and institutionalization.

Broad Essay

1037. (pp. 374-375, 395-397) (LD) Compare and contrast forms of collective behavior and social movements.

Major points: both are labels for collective activity; collective behavior refers to relatively unstructured and largely unpredictable activity, whereas social movements are more-or-less organized; social movements tend to be more concerted efforts at correcting some perceived inadequacy in existing social arrangements, and frequently develop leadership and specific goals as they are sustained over a longer period of time.

1038. (pp. 375-393) (LD) Describe the various kinds of crowds categorized in the text. Then show which of these kinds were present in the Watts riot.

Major points: kinds of crowds would be casual crowd, conventionalized crowd, active crowd, and expressive crowd. All of these kinds of crowds were present in the Watts riot. As the riot gained momentum, casual and conventionalized crowds became active and expressive crowds.

1039. (pp. 382-385) (MD) Explain why the exchange and spread of information by rumor is one of the most significant processes underlying the development of collective behavior. Also explain what is meant by the embedding pattern and compounding pattern of rumor distortion.

Major points: rumors play major role in collective behavior; they develop within context of ambiguity; these serially derived interpretations of reality may compensate for lack of objective definitions; embedding pattern: distortions that occur in serial retelling; elements are leveling, sharpening, and assimilation; compounding: rumors demand one another.

1040. (pp. 385-393) (MD) Show how the Watts riot illustrates the various elements in the social dynamics of collective behavior.

Major points: the elements to be discussed will be the inadequacies of existing structures, emotional contagion, rumor, and behavioral contagion.

CHAPTER 14. Mass Communication

Multiple Choice

1041. (p. 405) (MD) In discussing mass communications in a particular country in terms of interlocking components (such as ownership, content production, distribution, regulation, etc.), one is taking which of the perspectives below?
   a. cultural;
  *b. systems;
   c. analytical;
   d. inductive;
   e. deductive.

1042. (pp. 405-407) (LD) The components of a system of mass communication
       include all of the following except which one?
       a. ownership;
       b. control;
       c. audience;
     *d. consultants;
       e. distribution.

1043. (p. 407) (LD) The major development of the mass media in the United
       States occurred during:
       a. the first half of the nineteenth century;
       b. the period between World War I and World War II;
       c. the period since World War II;
       d. the last decade and a half;
     *e. the first half of the twentieth century.

1044. (p. 407) (LD) As a medium of mass communication, the daily news-
       paper reached its peak in terms of newspapers sold per household
       in the U.S.:
       a. during the American Civil War;
       b. just before the turn of the century;
     *c. at about the time of World War I;
       d. during World War II;
       e. during the last five years.

1045. (pp. 407-408) (LD) The resolution of which issue during the period
       of the Colonial Press has had the most influence on the American
       press today?
     *a. the First Amendment to the U.S. Constitution;
       b. reporters' rights of confidential sources;
       c. states' rights in voting laws;
       d. the freedom to advertise in the press;
       e. the right of a citizen to trial by jury.

1046. (pp. 407-408) (LD) The newspapers of the original thirteen colonies
       collectively called the Colonial Press were:
       a. much the same as those of the first decade of the twentieth
           century;
       b. like those we have today;
     *c. very different from those that developed during the last part
           of the nineteenth century;
       d. like those in smaller communities today;
       e. unlike the large daily newspapers of today, but very similar to
           such newspapers during the period 1890-1900.

1047. (p. 408) (MD) According to the text, the term mass press implies
       that a newspaper:
       a. is mass-produced by power presses so as to be readily available
           in large quantity;
       b. is sold in a mass society where people have weaker social ties
           to their fellows than in traditional societies;
       c. is sold to huge numbers of people, that is, to a mass audience;
     *d. depends mainly on advertising, entertaining content, and a large
           audience of ordinary people to make a profit;
       e. is very powerful in shaping public opinion on a mass basis.

1048. (p. 410) (LD) Among the following, which would be true of the American broadcast media?
    a. government control over content is minimal;
    b. they are based upon private ownership and the profit motive;
    c. they are supported principally by advertising;
    d. audiences exert strong indirect control over media content;
*e. all of the above.

1049. (p. 410) (LD) The central emphasis of the broadcast media in the United States is on:
    a. news reports;
*b. entertainment;
    c. documentaries;
    d. advertising;
    e. sensationalism.

1050. (pp. 410-411) (LD) The relationship between the news media and the government in the United States:
    a. is one continuous conflict;
    b. is a congenial relationship at all times;
    c. is one in which the news media are run by the government;
*d. is characterized by cooperation and conflict;
    e. is one of no real relationship between the news media and the government.

1051. (p. 413) (MD) The goals of the Soviet mass media include:
    a. developing class consciousness among people;
    b. increasing people's awareness of their cultural heritage;
    c. increasing private ownership of newspapers and radio;
    d. all of the above;
*e. only a and b above.

1052. (p. 414) (LD) Within the Soviet system of radio and TV today, which of the following is true?
    a. only trusted party officials are permitted to own shortwave radios that receive foreign broadcasts;
    b. foreign broadcasts on both long and shortwave are "jammed";
*c. most large cities now have TV channels;
    d. the ordinary citizen does not own a receiver but gets information on a "direct wire" speaker of poor quality;
    e. there is little to hear or see on Soviet broadcasting other than political propaganda.

1053. (p. 415) (MD) An individual's needs, attitudes, habits, values, and other psychological characteristics play a considerable part in determining the kinds of mass communications content. Sociologically, this is the principle of:
    a. stimulus-response;
    b. symbolism;
    c. internalization;
    d. congruence;
*e. selectivity.

1054. (p. 415) (LD) Psychological characteristics such as interests, attitudes, values, etc., determine in part how a person selects media content, interprets it, and acts upon it. The text accounts

for these characteristics as:
a. perceptual irregularities;
b. internalized factors;
c. socialization by-products;
*d. individual differences;
e. psychic variables.

1055. (p. 416) (MD) Which of the following is not an important factor in
the selective attention, perception, and action of an audience
toward mass communication?
a. attitude consistency;
*b. simplicity of presentation;
c. supportive values;
d. congruence with beliefs;
e. level of interest.

1056. (p. 417) (MD) It has been found that the heaviest readers of the
"true confessions" type of magazine are younger married women with
lower levels of income and educational attainment who reside in
small towns in the Midwest and South. This illustrates the influence on mass communication of:
*a. social categories;
b. individual differences;
c. value indicators;
d. integrated groups;
e. cultural norms.

1057. (p. 417) (LD) Patterns of attending to and consumption of mass
communication content are roughly similar for people who are similar
regarding such variables as age, sex, income, occupation, etc. This
fact is referred to as the influence of:
a. collective behavior;
b. social organization;
c. culture traits;
d. personal organization;
*e. social categories.

1058. (p. 418) (MD) John Smith depends for his information concerning
recent political issues on a close group of friends at work. In
fact, he usually relies for most of his ideas on one of his buddies
who reads the newspaper a lot. Such behavior illustrates:
a. the social categories influence process;
b. the significance of peer groups at work;
c. the social input factor in interaction;
d. the diffusion of innovation theory;
*e. the two-step flow of communication.

1059. (p. 418) (LD) The mass communication process seems to depend considerably upon informal interpersonal relationships. An example
would be the case where key communicators attend to the media, pass
on information to others, and help shape their interpretations of
media messages. Sociologists refer to the latter as:
a. social control;
b. psychological structuring;
c. stimulus-response;

    d. mass persuasion;
   *e. personal influence.

1060. (pp. 418-420) (MD) Joseph Klapper's comprehensive review of
       accumulated research on the effects of the mass media on <u>individuals</u>
       yielded all of the following generalizations <u>except</u> which one?
      *a. there are numerous occasions in which mass communications do
           seem to produce direct effects;
       b. mass communication is usually not a necessary and sufficient
           cause of audience effects;
       c. mass communication is usually a contributory agent which re-
           inforces rather than changes some condition;
       d. mass communications achieve influence among and through a set
           of mediatory factors;
       e. the way in which mass communication achieves effects depends
           upon numerous indirect factors (e.g., source of message, type
           of medium).

1061. (p. 422) (LD) People who belong to the Republican party attend
       faithfully to the speeches of their party's candidates and hear views
       which they feel coincide with and support their convictions. This
       illustrates the:
      *a. reinforcement effect;
       b. media bias principle;
       c. direct effect concept;
       d. two-step flow;
       e. conversion phenomenon.

1062. (pp. 422-426) (MD) As regards the contribution of the mass media
       to our major social ills, social scientists have concluded that:
       a. cultural tastes are clearly on the decline because of the low
           level of television content;
       b. the media have no other responsibility than to operate as
           profit-making enterprises within the American legal structure;
      *c. the media's emphasis on violence, crime, and other forms of
           deviance is having an effect on some categories of viewers;
       d. the media must accept their responsibility to raise esthetic
           standards in our society;
       e. none of the above.

1063. (pp. 426-427) (LD) Persuasive campaigns in which media messages
       are designed to alter such variables as fears, attitudes, sex
       urges, vanity, etc., in the hope that the individual will take
       action because of these alterations are based on the:
       a. psychological factors postulate;
      *b. psychodynamic approach;
       c. unconscious motivations hypothesis;
       d. personal influence theory;
       e. internal expectation system.

1064. (pp. 426-428) (MD) A mass media campaign is designed to change
       people's attitudes toward members of a minority group to a more
       favorable position. If the campaign is successful in achieving
       such a change, it can be safely predicted that such people:

a. will definitely reduce their level of discrimination (negative overt action) toward that group;

b. will normally become more discriminatory toward other similar groups but less so toward the group in question;

c. will reduce levels of discrimination toward all such minority groups, at least to some extent;

d. will reduce discrimination toward ethnic minorities but not toward racial minorities;

*e. may or may not reduce their level of discrimination (negative overt action) toward that group.

1065. (p. 428) (LD) The local Community Fund solicits donations by announcing goals (quotas), setting group norms, defining various roles, sanctions for failing to give, etc. Such a persuasion campaign is based on:

a. role-counterrole procedures;

b. submerged guilt complexes;

c. unconscious communication;

*d. a sociocultural strategy;

e. all of the above.

1066. (p. 429) (MD) Perhaps the best way of summing up the way the sociocultural strategy of persuasion works is to say that:

a. it creates deep-seated disequilibria in the functioning of the personality and a way of restoring those equilibria;

*b. it provides the potential donor with a "definition of the situation" concerning norms, roles, sanctions, and approved values;

c. it links attitudes and behavior together in a highly correlated system, so that changes in attitudes yield corresponding changes in behavior;

d. it plays upon the sympathies of people for the underdog and gets them to act on this basis;

e. it does all of the above.

1067. (p. 429) (MD) Close examination of the significance of the mass media concerning the formation and control of public opinion reveals that the media:

a. play little or no part in the formation of public opinion in democracies;

b. have overwhelming power to form or alter public opinion in all societies;

c. are important influence on public opinion only in totalitarian regimes;

d. have little influence on public opinion in any type of society;

*e. play an important part in the formation and crystallization of public opinion in democracies.

1068. (p. 429) (LD) The theoretical construct used by sociologists for a large number of people--such as the population of a nation--who have no ties of social organization to each other is a:

*a. mass;

b. category;

c. society;

d. audience;

e. multitude.

1069. (p. 430) (MD) A research procedure for studying individuals' attitudes, preferences, and other predispositions is:
    a. content analysis;
    b. laboratory experiments;
    c. field experiments;
    d. participant observation;
    *e. opinion polling.

1070. (p. 430) (LD) Valid and reliable opinion polls require proper sampling. All of the following practices have generally resulted in accurate sampling except:
    a. computers;
    b. professional pollsters;
    *c. telephone polls;
    d. door-to-door sampling;
    e. the above sampling practices have always been accurate.

1071. (p. 431) (MD) A large number of people learn that a major political candidate has had prior psychiatric treatment. Many do not know how to respond to this, and consequently, focus attention on it. From the standpoint of public-opinion theory formation such people are at this point:
    *a. a public;
    b. a mass;
    c. an aggregate;
    d. a category;
    e. a bloc.

1072. (p. 431) (LD) The principle that people use definitions obtained in interaction with others in order to assign meaning to unstructured events is called the:
    a. definitional process;
    *b. reality principle;
    c. meaning hypothesis;
    d. interactive procedure;
    e. structuring source.

1073. (p. 434) (LD) A newly formulated and shared (normative) conviction of the members of a public concerning the appropriate way to interpret a controversial event can be called:
    *a. public opinion;
    b. collective delusion;
    c. private opinion;
    d. mass interpretation;
    e. audience attitude.

1074. (p. 435) (LD) If a population has had experience with an unstructured situation of a given type and has created norms to interpret and respond to it, other situations of this type can be more easily handled. This function of public opinion is called the:
    a. social guidance function;
    b. normative formation function;
    *c. cultural adaptation function;
    d. collective resolution function;
    e. issue simplification function.

1075. (p. 436) (LD) When public opinion is unified on a given issue, it serves to integrate the goals of a community or society. This activity of public opinion is referred to as the:
 *a. social solidarity function;
  b. unification function;
  c. homogenization function;
  d. issue clarification function;
  e. conflict reduction function.

True-False

1076. (p. 409) (MD) Though similar in many respects, the operating assumption of the press differs from the broadcast media in the U.S. in that the broadcast media have traditionally been subject to government licensing and regulation while the press has not.
 *a. true;
  b. false.

1077. (p. 409) (MD) Advertisers have a greater influence on content in broadcasting than in newspaper publishing.
 *a. true;
  b. false.

1078. (p. 410) (LD) The textbook states that the central emphasis of the broadcast media in the United States is on advertising.
  a. true;
 *b. false.

1079. (pp. 410-411) (LD) A major point of controversy over the social responsibility of the mass media concerns the fact that the media consist of generally profit-making commercial enterprises.
 *a. true;
  b. false.

1080. (p. 413) (LD) Prior to the communist revolution in Russia, the culture of that society included a belief in freedom of expression something like that found in English-speaking countries.
  a. true;
 *b. false.

1081. (p. 416) (LD) The experiment by Kendall and Wolfe, which dealt with a campaign to reduce prejudice through the use of cartoons, showed that many people misinterpreted the cartoons and thought the cartoons supported their prejudices.
 *a. true;
  b. false.

1082. (p. 416) (LD) Research reported in the textbook suggests that the mass media are more likely to reinforce existing popular attitudes than to change them.
 *a. true;
  b. false.

1083. (p. 416) (LD) Patterns of attention to, and consumption of, mass communication content are roughly similar among people of the same age, sex, income, and religion.

*a. true;
 b. false.

1084. (p. 422) (MD) A well-known study of the presidential election of 1940 showed that preelection publicity and propaganda changed the voting intentions only of those voters who had made up their minds early, before being exposed to the media.
 a. true;
*b. false.

1085. (p. 422) (MD) Research has shown that such relationships as friendship have little or no influence on an audience that is relatively homogeneous in social traits.
 a. true;
*b. false.

1086. (p. 422) (LD) By the "status conferral" effect of mass media, we mean the tendency for the mere coverage of an event or personality to bestow status or credibility on that event or personality.
*a. true;
 b. false.

1087. (p. 426) (LD) As used in the study of mass communications, the term propaganda carries a negative connotation, whereas the term education has a positive connotation.
 a. true;
*b. false.

1088. (p. 427) (LD) One of the repeated findings of mass communications research is that once an attitude has been changed we can be quite sure that behavior will also change, and in the same general direction.
 a. true;
*b. false.

1089. (p. 429) (MD) The ability of any mass communication system to convert people from one set of ideas to another depends mainly upon that system's total control or monopoly over information and propaganda dissemination.
*a. true;
 b. false.

1090. (p. 429) (MD) The textbook contends that, in spite of the relative "openness" of our democratic system, public opinion can be pretty thoroughly manipulated by the mass media.
 a. true;
*b. false.

1091. (p. 429) (LD) In the sociology of mass communication, the term mass suggests the complete absence of any social organization.
*a. true;
 b. false.

1092. (pp. 429-431) (LD) In sociological usage, the terms mass and public mean about the same thing.

a.   true;
*b.   false.

1093.   (p. 431) (LD)   When people are confronted with an ambiguous event
or a lack of relevant information and norms, they usually try to
establish orienting frames of reference through interaction with
others.
*a.   true;
b.   false.

1094.   (p. 431) (MD)   One of the concepts used in the study of public
opinion is the so-called reality principle--that public or social
definitions of reality are the definitions people are likely to use.
*a.   true;
b.   false.

1095.   (p. 434) (MD)   The use of the mass media to promote social solidarity
is more important in urban industrial societies than it is in more
homogeneous rural ones, which tend to have unified public opinion
on most issues anyway.
*a.   true;
b.   false.

Fill-In

1096.   (p. 410) (LD)   The mass communication system in the _____
is characterized by private ownership of the media.

United States

1097.   (p. 415) (MD)   The _____ _____ refers to the way
an individual's pattern of needs, attitudes, habits, and values
determines what he or she will selectively attend to in his or her
environment.

principle of selectivity

1098.   (p. 416) (MD)   Audience members who have similar _____
_____ will share common orientations and patterns of usage
concerning the mass media.

social characteristics

1099.   (p. 426) (LD)   _____ can be defined as message content that
is designed to be persuasive.

Propaganda

1100.   (p. 427) (MD)   The _____ strategy of mass persuasion concentrates on defining or redefining certain patterns of expectation
that serve as behavioral guides for members of groups.

sociocultural

1101.   (p. 429) (LD)   A _____ is a large number of individuals who
exist within a society but who have no social connections with one
another.

mass

Matching

1102. (pp. 407-418) (LD)
    media in the U.S.   privately owned
    media in the U.S.S.R.   government owned
    individual differences in   principle of selectivity
      response to stimuli
    similar social characteristics   share common orientations
    informal interpersonal relations   two-step flow of communication

1103. (pp. 418-422) (MD)
    creative effects   people have few prior attitudes
                                     about an issue
    conversion   very seldom possible
    minor changes   relatively frequent
    reinforcement   selection of material con-
                                       sistent with beliefs--
                                       "mental callouses"

1104. (pp. 426-428) (MD)
    persuasion   achieve behavioral change
                                       through communication
    propaganda   message content designed to
                                       be persuasive
    psychodynamic persuasion   attitudes correlated with
                                       overt behavior
    sociocultural persuasion   creation of many roles and
                                       counterroles
    mass communication   achieves influence through
                                       mediating factors

1105. (pp. 429-435) (LD)
    mass   large numbers of individuals
                                         with no social connections
    public   shared attention is a necessary
                                         condition
    public opinion   sociological concept
    individual opinion   psychological concept
    public opinion   may help integrate a society
                                       behind collective goals

Short Essay

1106. (pp. 407-415) (LD) Briefly describe the difference between the mass communication systems in the U.S. and the U.S.S.R.

Major points: American system is based upon private ownership and is dedicated to corporate profit while the Soviet system is not. Also, the Soviet system is rigidly controlled by government.

1107. (pp. 418-426) (MD) Describe the types of effects mass communications may have on attitudes and opinions.

Major points: creative effects, reinforcement, minor change, conversion, and no effect.

1108. (pp. 426-428) (LD) Define persuasion. Then pick one of the strategies employed in a persuasion campaign and briefly describe it.

Major points: attempt to achieve some form of behavioral change on the part of an audience through communication; strategies may be psychodynamic or sociocultural.

1109. (pp. 435-436) (MD) Discuss three functions of public opinion.

Major points: cultural adaptation, social control, and social solidarity.

Broad Essay

1110. (pp. 407-415) (LD) Contrast the mass communication systems in the U.S. and the U.S.S.R. with particular reference to their differing social and cultural traditions.

Major points: in the United States, central emphasis is on entertainment; mass communication is characterized by private ownership and is dedicated to corporate profits; in the U.S.S.R., mass communication is not concerned with profit, and doesn't represent private enterprise; doesn't provide entertainment but is conceived as a channel of communication between the party and the masses.

1111. (pp. 415-418) (MD) Discuss the three intervening variables thought to modify or mediate the impact that message content can have on the behavior of a receiving audience member.

Major points: the influence of individual differences, social categories, and social relationships.

1112. (pp. 418-426) (MD) Discuss the major <u>direct</u> and <u>indirect</u> effects of the media in our society.

Major points: media are important agents of social and cultural change; the direct effects can be creative, reinforcing, or minor; indirect effects include status conferral, definition of events, and definitions of the situation which may be viewed as normative.

1113. (pp. 426-428) (LD) Name and discuss two general strategies that have been developed for a persuasion campaign.

Major points: psychodynamic persuasion: attempts to alter psychological variables in such a way that the individual will respond overtly in ways desired; sociocultural persuasion: concentrates on defining or redefining certain patterns of expectation that serve as behavioral guides for members of groups.

CHAPTER 15. Marriage and the Family

Multiple Choice

1114. (p. 440) (LD) According to the textbook, which of the following is the most fundamental kind of social institution?

a. religious;
b. political;
c. economic;
d. educational;
*e. familial.

1115. (p. 440) (MD) An important activity of the family is to transmit to offspring material goods and social status. This probably is best seen in traditional societies, where wealth and status depend more heavily upon:
a. rigid laws regarding inheritance;
b. a lack of inheritance taxes;
c. an agricultural economy;
d. mores that prescribe power relationships;
*e. ascribed characteristics.

1116. (p. 440) (MD) In modern urban-industrial societies:
*a. the division of labor between males and females has become blurred;
b. male dominance is still considered part of the "natural order";
c. marriage is one of the few remaining areas of harmony in society;
d. sex roles of marriage partners are no longer complementary;
e. a, b, and c only.

1117. (p. 440) (LD) The traditional activities of the family regarding the transmission of material goods and social status are probably less important in what type of society?
a. agricultural society;
b. peasant society;
c. primitive society;
*d. industrialized society;
e. military society.

1118. (p. 441) (LD) Marriage laws and customs in all societies are:
a. nearly identical;
b. immutable (unchangeable);
*c. generally successful;
d. all of the above;
e. none of the above.

1119. (p. 442) (LD) While various forms of marriage have been found among peoples of the world, the one that occurs in all societies and is predominant even when other forms exist is:
*a. monogamy;
b. polygyny;
c. polyandry;
d. matriarchy;
e. patriarchy.

1120. (pp. 442-443) (LD) The terms patriarchy, matriarchy, egalitarian, matrilineal, patrilineal, matrilocal, neolocal, and so on, refer to:
a. the pattern of allocation of authority in the family;
b. the way in which families transfer property to their next generation;
c. parental obligations in child-rearing;

    d. the location or pattern of residence of various members of the family;

 *e. one or another of the above.

1121. (p. 442) (LD) A family consisting of the husband, the wife, and their immediate children is called:

 *a. nuclear;
  b. extended;
  c. basic;
  d. companionate;
  e. independent.

1122. (p. 442) (LD) Which of the following kinds of family would be most likely to have grandparents included in the residence?

  a. patriarchal;
  b. consanguine;
 *c. extended;
  d. nuclear;
  e. neolocal.

1123. (p. 442) (MD) The Jones family consists of Milton and Lois Jones, their two children Nancy and Roger, plus the grandparents Charles and Bessie, and Milton's brother and sister, Uncle Armand and Aunt Marilyn, each of whom has several children. They all live in the same town. Such a family would be classified sociologically as:

 *a. consanguine;
  b. egalitarian;
  c. nuclear;
  d. virilocal;
  e. patriarchal.

1124. (pp. 442-443) (MD) Ed Smith was a somewhat "henpecked" man; his wife ran things pretty much as she wanted. He recently died and left everything to his son, who had just moved to another city with his new wife. This left Mrs. Smith penniless. The Smith family was clearly:

  a. matriarchal;
  b. neolocal;
  c. patrilineal;
 *d. all of the above;
  e. only a and c above.

1125. (p. 445) (LD) The early Christians took a clear position on the issue of male versus female dominance. Which of the following best expresses that position?

 *a. strict patriarchy;
  b. strict matriarchy;
  c. egalitarian family;
  d. male dominance in economic matters mainly;
  e. female dominance in domestic and child-rearing issues.

1126. (p. 446) (LD) Among the Hopi, the blood relatives are traced through the female line. This indicates that their family organization is:

  a. matriarchal;
 *b. matrilineal;

c. matrioptimal;
d. matricentered;
e. all of the above.

1127. (p. 446) (MD) Hopi customs involve trying to prevent:
a. divorce;
b. loss of female virginity;
*c. marriage within clan or phratry;
d. all of the above;
e. only <u>a</u> and <u>b</u>.

1128. (p. 446) (LD) Among the Hopi, divorce is:
a. unheard of;
b. known but strongly disapproved;
c. accepted only because of sexual infidelity;
*d. accepted with little fanfare;
e. becoming somewhat more common with increased industrialization.

1129. (p. 448) (MD) The status of women in Hopi society is relatively
high compared to their status in other traditional societies. This
can be attributed to:
a. matrilineal structure;
b. matrilocal residence;
c. matricentered discipline over children;
d. all three of the above;
*e. only <u>a</u> and <u>b</u> above.

1130. (p. 448) (LD) In Hopi society, a man serves as a source of discipline for:
a. his sons;
b. his younger brothers;
c. his cousins;
*d. his newphews;
e. his grandchildren.

1131. (p. 449) (MD) Which of the following combinations of societies are
similar in that to a large extent the meaning of individual behavior
is found in the contribution it makes to group well-being?
a. ancient Greece and ancient Hebrews;
b. early Christians and contemporary America;
c. ancient Hebrews and the Hopi;
*d. the Hopi and contemporary Chinese;
e. Chinese and the United States.

1132. (pp. 452-453) (MD) During the colonial period the laws regarding
sexual behavior in the North and South were:
a. identical in many respects;
b. more lenient in the North than in the South;
*c. more lenient in the South than in the North;
d. not based on religious beliefs;
e. based on religious beliefs only in the South.

1133. (p. 453) (MD) Among the Puritans of the Massachusetts Bay Colony,
adultery was legally punishable by:
a. dunking;
b. fines;

c. public rebuke;
*d. death;
e. whipping.

1134. (p. 453) (LD) In general, colonial laws regarding sexual behavior
could be characterized as:
a. varying greatly by state;
b. lenient;
c. rather uniform from state to state;
*d. severe;
e. only a and d above.

1135. (pp. 453-466) (LD) William Ogburn saw the dilemma of modern times
as the loss of many of the traditional activities of the family due
to the influence of:
*a. industrialization and urbanization;
b. freedom and promiscuity;
c. premarital sex and divorce;
d. violence and militarism;
e. secularization and immorality.

1136. (p. 453) (MD) In his analysis of the changing activities of the
family, William Ogburn concluded that:
a. contemporary families now perform about the same activities
that they did in colonial times;
*b. modern families have ceased many of the activities they performed
for their members in earlier centuries;
c. the greatest change in family activities has been the decline in
the role of the family in distributing affection and forming
personality;
d. modern families perform many more activities for their members
than was the case in colonial times;
e. modern families have literally lost all of their former activities.

1137. (p. 456) (LD) Murdock's study of 250 societies revealed that the
production of food, shelter, and clothing was widely found as a
family activity. In contemporary society:
a. the family differs little from those Murdock studied;
*b. the family is mainly a consuming unit;
c. the family is both a producing and a consuming unit;
d. the family is losing its activities as a consuming unit;
e. the family has never been a consuming or a producing unit.

1138. (p. 456) (LD) Which of the following continues to be an important
family activity in industrialized societies?
a. mate selection;
b. production of material goods;
c. adult socialization for the family of orientation;
*d. consumption of goods and services;
e. all except a above.

1139. (pp. 456-457) (LD) Industrialization and urbanization have changed
family patterns in all except which of the following activities?
a. protective activities;
b. socialization practices;

c. economic activities;
d. religious activities;
*e. all of the above have been changed.

1140. (p. 456) (LD) The influence of family socialization on young adults is particularly evident in:
*a. mate selection and political outlook;
b. reading habits and clothing tastes;
c. musical taste and food preferences;
d. attitudes toward drugs and furniture styles;
e. sexual attitudes and cooking skills.

1141. (p. 459) (LD) Since the family has undergone such radical changes, some scholars argue that the nuclear family is:
a. bound to restore some of its functions;
b. going to disappear;
c. not going to change any further;
d. less important to individuals;
*e. in a state of crisis.

1142. (p. 459) (LD) According to sociologists cited in the text, the modern family has as its main activity:
a. developing a self-sufficient economic unit;
b. providing educational experiences for the young;
c. protective activities for young and old members;
d. giving a religious foundation to life;
*e. companionship, affection, and personality formation.

1143. (pp. 460-461) (LD) The various differences in social background that might reduce chances for marital success include which of the following?
a. social class;
b. ethnicity;
c. religion;
*d. all of the above;
e. only a and b.

1144. (p. 460) (MD) Most religious groups strongly oppose interfaith marriages. The reasons cited for this commonly include all of the following except which one?
a. such marriages bring clashes in fundamental values;
b. such marriages bring conflict over the religious training of children;
*c. such marriages lead to a decline in church activity for one or both parents;
d. such marriages lead to conflicting loyalties between church and relatives;
e. such marriages may suffer spiritually.

1145. (p. 460) (MD) All of the following factors have been found to influence rates of interfaith marriage except:
a. relative size of religious group in community;
b. attitudes of prejudice;
c. socioeconomic and status differences;
d. degree of ethnic cohesiveness;
*e. all above influence interfaith marriage rates.

1146. (p. 462) (MD) John (from a wealthy, rural, Catholic family) and
      Susan (from a poor, urban, Jewish family) decide to marry. Using
      the findings of sociological research, what prediction should be
      made for the probable success of this particular marriage?
      *a. the greater the sociocultural differences between partners,
           the less likely the chances for success. However, predictions
           of individual cases (as opposed to proportions in a category)
           are unwarranted. Thus no prediction should be made;
       b. such a marriage is bound to fail sooner or later because of the
           generalization cited in a above;
       c. such a marriage is bound to succeed on the grounds that unlike
           people are more attractive to one another. The generalization
           cited in a is nonsense;
       d. sociologists have not assembled information on these issues, so
           predictions are impossible;
       e. because of the generalization cited in a above, we can say only
           that this particular marriage will probably fail.

1147. (p. 463) (MD) According to sociologists who have attempted to study
      the basis of mature and fulfilling love, the most important basis
      of such a relationship is:
      *a. mutual feelings of social equality and performing reciprocal
           acts for one another;
       b. "cardiac-respiratory" responses in the presence of the other
           person;
       c. a sufficient economic base so that money is no problem;
       d. very strong sexual responses to each other;
       e. a very romantic orientation to the sex act on the part of the
           female.

1148. (p. 463) (LD) An increasingly important basis for satisfaction in
      modern marriages is:
       a. economic interdependence;
       b. religious similarities;
      *c. reciprocal conjugal love;
       d. youth;
       e. leisure time together.

1149. (p. 464) (LD) About what proportion of American couples never get
      divorced?
       a. about half;
       b. about one in four;
      *c. about three out of four;
       d. about one in ten;
       e. about nine out of ten.

1150. (p. 464) (LD) Sociologists have found that the relationship between
      economic status and the divorce rate is:
       a. direct but weak;
      *b. indirect (or inverse);
       c. direct and strongly positive;
       d. nonexistent;
       e. spurious.

1151. (pp. 464-465) (LD) Widowed women must face which of the following
      problems?

a. insufficient support and income;
b. lack of preparation for the work world;
c. social isolation;
d. higher propensity to such problems as mental illness and suicide;
*e. all of the above.

1152. (p. 466) (MD) Teenage dating is discussed in the text within the context of leisure and recreation. The position taken by the text is that:
a. dating should be strictly supervised by parents;
b. parents should exercise no control whatever over teenage dating;
*c. a latent function of dating is socialization for future mate selection and family roles;
d. dating should be viewed as a form of recreation but not socialization;
e. dating should be postponed until the young person is at least sixteen years old.

1153. (p. 466) (MD) Most sociological research supports the generalization that in the U.S. sexual "promiscuity," in the sense of a female's accepting many men prior to marriage, is:
a. almost nonexistent;
b. declining greatly;
*c. more common than it ever was;
d. declining modestly;
e. almost universal.

1154. (p. 466) (LD) When negative sanctions for premarital coitus are heavy for the female and light or nonexistent for the male, sociologists define the situation as:
a. normal;
b. abnormal;
c. one-sided;
*d. a double standard;
e. an ideal.

1155. (p. 466) (MD) Research conducted during the last quarter century supports which of the following conclusions?
a. virginity among poor and working-class women is less common today;
b. since World War II college students have become less permissive in their sexual attitudes and behavior;
c. coital activity among college-educated young people is similar to that among those who have not attended college;
d. some 90 percent of young people who have premarital intercourse marry each other;
*e. only a and c.

1156. (p. 468) (MD) Research reported in the text indicates that the most strongly ingrained identity in people is their:
a. religious affiliation;
b. ancestry;
c. ethnic identity;
*d. sex gender identity;
e. educational identity.

1157. (pp. 468-469) (LD) Contemporary research on human sexuality suggests that:
    a. males are naturally dominant while females are submissive;
    b. early anatomical development in fetuses is female;
    c. the religious belief of Eve-out-of-Adam has been supported;
    d. women have at least as great a capacity for orgasm as men;
    *e. b and d only.

True-False

1158. (p. 441) (MD) The authors point out early in the chapter on the family that ethnocentrism has a lot to do with people's attitudes toward different kinds of sexual behavior in their own societies but not in exotic ones.
    a. true;
    *b. false.

1159. (pp. 442-444) (MD) Divorce is a modern invention; it was not practiced by ancient Hebrews, Greeks, and Romans.
    a. true;
    *b. false.

1160. (p. 444) (LD) Male homosexuality was an acceptable form of sexual behavior among ancient Greeks.
    *a. true;
    b. false.

1161. (p. 445) (MD) The ancient Hebrew family pattern was the closest to the "ideal type" of the patriarchal family.
    a. true;
    *b. false.

1162. (p. 445) (LD) Male dominance was preached by Christian leaders such as St. Paul and St. Augustine.
    *a. true;
    b. false.

1163. (p. 445) (MD) In comparing Jewish scriptures with Christian ones, it is clear that the Jewish teachings (as in the Old Testament) were much more strict and harsh with regard to sex and marriage.
    a. true;
    *b. false.

1164. (p. 446) (LD) Compared to other traditional societies, the Hopi Indians accord fairly high status to women.
    *a. true;
    b. false.

1165. (p. 446) (MD) The Hopi form of family life is affected somewhat by the fact that, compared to other Indian tribes, the Hopi enjoy a fairly high degree of affluence.
    a. true;
    *b. false.

1166. (p. 448) (MD) Although the Hopi vest the authority to make decisions in the female line, the important decisions are actually made by the

males, just as in most Western societies.
*a. true;
 b. false.

1167. (p. 456) (MD) Murdock's worldwide study of the family institution
        in various societies shows that family organization always combines
        the rights and privileges of sexual intercourse with norms and roles
        for a division of labor designed to satisfy the needs for food,
        shelter, and clothing.
        *a. true;
         b. false.

1168. (p. 456) (LD) In terms of economic activity the family in modern
        industrialized societies is primarily a productive unit.
         a. true;
        *b. false.

1169. (p. 456) (LD) The family has lost all of its socialization and
        educational functions because of urbanization and industrialization.
         a. true;
        *b. false.

1170. (pp. 456-457) (MD) The family's central role in forming individuals'
        political personalities derives from its role as the main source
        for the satisfaction of their needs. Children therefore tend to
        identify with their parents and to adopt their outlook toward
        politics.
        *a. true;
         b. false.

1171. (pp. 456-457) (LD) Though some aspects of parent-child relations
        have changed in recent years, the reciprocal role obligations of
        parents and children have actually increased.
         a. true;
        *b. false.

1172. (p. 457) (MD) Sociologists know of no contemporary society that
        has effectively utilized the aged.
         a. true;
        *b. false.

1173. (p. 457) (MD) Social research has indicated that the old saying
        that "families that pray together stay together" is false.
         a. true;
        *b. false.

1174. (p. 460) (MD) In spite of increasing interfaith contacts, inter-
        faith marriages have shown little or no increase in recent years.
         a. true;
        *b. false.

1175. (p. 461) (LD) If current trends continue, sociologists predict a
        great increase in interracial marriages in the late 1970s.
         a. true;
        *b. false.

1176. (p. 462) (LD) According to the findings of sociologists, the greater
the sociocultural differences between the partners, the less likely
are chances for success in marriage.
    *a. true;
    b.   false.

1177. (p. 463) (MD) Sociological studies of the part played by "romantic
love" in modern marriage suggest that it has little to do with
satisfactory marital adjustment.
    *a. true;
    b.   false.

1178. (p. 469) (LD) Most research supports the contention that women's
social subordination to men is based on biology.
    a.   true;
    *b. false.

Fill-In

1179. (p. 442) (LD) The most common form of marriage is _____.

    monogamy

1180. (p. 442) (LD) For children, the nuclear family is the _____
of _____ because they are biologically related to all the
other members.

    family, orientation

1181. (p. 464) (MD) Divorce terminates about _____ out of
_____ new marriages.

    four, ten

1182. (p. 443) (MD) The most common form of polygamy is _____.

    polygyny

1183. (p. 466) (LD) A _____ _____ exists when the
negative sanctions for premarital coitus are heavy for the female
and light for the male.

    double standard

1184. (p. 466) (MD) Today in our society, the manifest purpose of dating
is _____.

    recreation

Matching

1185. (pp. 442-443) (MD)
    monogamy   one man, one woman
    polygyny   one man, more than one woman
    polyandry   one woman, more than one man
    consanguine   biologically related
    egalitarian   emerging family pattern

1186. (pp. 442-443) (MD)
 nuclear family for parents   family of procreation
 nuclear family for children   consanguine
 dominant form of authority   patriarchy
 least common form of authority matriarchy
 emerging family pattern   egalitarian

1187. (pp. 461-465) (LD)
 interethnic marriages   25 to 40 percent
 interracial marriages   less than one percent
 religiously endogamous Catholics three out of four
 likelihood of males losing   low
  partners through death
 likelihood of more divorces for high
  those occupying lower economic
  strata

1188. (pp. 453-466) (MD)
 severe penalties on sexual behavior Puritan heritage
 consumption of goods   changes in earning a living
 limits courtship and mate selection influence of family social-
               ization
 recreation   manifest purpose of dating
 no basis for predicting increase interracial marriage

Short Essay

1189. (pp. 442-459) (MD) Describe two of the ways in which the activities of the American family are changing.

Major points: answer will vary according to which of the following is picked: earning a living, education, begetting children, religion, protection, choosing a marriage partner, love and sex.

1190. (pp. 442-443) (LD) Briefly define the different forms of marriage that may occur.

Major points: monogamy and polygamy (this form will also include polygyny and polyandry).

1191. (pp. 442-443) (MD) Briefly define the different types of authority, types of residence, and types of descent possible in a family.

Major points: patriarchy, matriarchy, egalitarian, patrilineal, matrilineal, bilateral, matrilocal, patrilocal, and neolocal.

1192. (p. 467) (LD) Describe some of the advantages of, and the problems associated with, self-administered questionnaires.

Major points: advantages include reaching a large number of respondents with a limited budget, privacy for the respondent, and standardized format; problems are the low return rate, variety of interpretations of questions, and level of difficulty of questions.

Broad Essay

1193. (pp. 442-451) (MD) Give a brief historical sketch of family patterns in the Western world from the ancient Hebrews to contemporary America and compare these patterns to modern Chinese family organization.

Major points: the ancient Hebrews, Greeks, and Romans had patriarchal and patrilineal family patterns with monogamous marriage structures; in varying degrees divorce was permitted; in China the Marriage Law of 1950 abolished the traditional patriarchal, patrilineal system based on the clan structure and created a collectivistic ideology. The American family today traces its male dominance to the Colonial period.

1194. (pp. 445-459) (MD) Compare the Hopi Indian family in form of marriage, degree of independence of the marital unit, and patterns of family organization with a typical family in an industrial society.

Major points: monogamy, extended and nuclear family, matrilineal, matrilocal residence.

1195. (pp. 453-463) (LD) From the text, it was noted that certain aspects of the American family are undergoing change. Describe at least six of these changes and give possible explanations for them.

Major points: answer will vary according to which of the following is picked: earning a living, education, begetting children, religious aspect, protection and governing behavior, choosing a marriage partner, love and sex.

1196. (p. 464) (LD) One consequence of the changes taking place in the United States has been the rise in divorce rates. Summarize briefly and discuss the main points concerning divorce in the U.S.

Major points: occurs mostly among young persons; increase in divorce particularly due to reasons other than the growth of the married population; U.S.A. has the highest rate of divorce.

CHAPTER 16. Religion

Multiple Choice

1197. (p. 470) (LD) To Durkheim, the "sacred" represents things and ideas considered worthy of profound respect and honor. He called everything else:
  a. irreligious;
  b. nonsacred;
  c. secular;
  *d. profane;
  e. this-worldly.

1198. (p. 471) (MD) The textbook discusses several dimensions of religiosity which include all of the following except:
  *a. superstition;
  b. ritual;
  c. knowledge;

    d. experience;
    e. belief.

1199. (p. 471) (LD) Studies of religious groups, such as the survey by
       Glock and Stark of over 3000 members of various Christian churches,
       indicate that:
   *a. even among church members, a large number had doubts of one
       kind or another concerning the existence of God;
    b. belief that "Jesus is the Divine Son of God" was truly universal;
    c. reports of miracles (walking on water, etc.) were not questioned;
    d. the concept of a life beyond death was the only belief accepted
       by all;
    e. biblical accounts of the birth of Jesus were regarded as com-
       pletely true.

1200. (pp. 471-476) (MD) The examination of the religious beliefs of
       over 3000 members of Christian churches by Glock and Stark showed
       that:
    a. church membership is declining in the United States;
    b. people are turning more and more to basic Christian beliefs;
    c. churches have failed in American society;
   *d. belonging to a church may have little to do with fundamental
       belief in Christian theology;
    e. people truly need religious beliefs in order to carry on their
       daily lives.

1201. (p. 473) (MD) According to the textbook, rituals serve which of
       the following purposes?
    a. designating the members' duties and responsibilities;
    b. symbolically presenting part of the faith;
    c. honoring the divinity or divinities worshipped;
    d. b and c only;
   *e. a, b, and c.

1202. (pp. 473-475) (MD) In the Church of Jesus in Jolo, West Virginia,
       rattlesnakes are regularly handled under the conviction that if one
       truly has the faith, such serpents pose no threat to the handler.
       Such practices illustrate which of the following dimensions of
       religiosity?
    a. ideological;
    b. experiential;
   *c. ritualistic;
    d. revelational;
    e. sacred.

1203. (p. 476) (MD) Eliza Smith was walking along the seashore one after-
       noon when she suddenly felt that she was in the presence of a divine
       force. Because of this experience she suddenly knew that her reli-
       gious beliefs were really true. A sociology student of religious
       behavior would probably classify this as:
   *a. a "confirming" experience;
    b. revelation;
    c. an ecstatic experience;
    d. nonsense or hysteria;
    e. a charismatic experience.

1204. (p. 477) (LD) The textbook discusses several forms of experience in which believers have some form of contact with the supernatural. The type of experience in which individuals feel they have received a sacred message is called:
    a. a "confirming" experience;
    b. a visitation;
    c. a charismatic experience;
    d. an ecstatic experience;
  *e. revelation.

1205. (p. 477) (MD) Ann M. spent most of her life as an invalid. While many people regard her life as tragic, she was normally cheerful, explaining that her illness was "part of God's plan" and as such was very meaningful to her. Such a view illustrates:
    a. the experiential dimension of religiosity;
    b. the ritualistic aspect of faith;
    c. a well-known neurotic syndrome;
    d. the power of spiritism;
  *e. the "security" function of religion.

1206. (p. 477) (LD) When sociologists refer to the "functions of religiosity" they are, in effect, referring to:
    a. the causes of religious commitment and belief;
    b. the way in which the individual comes to accept religion;
    c. the specific content of an individual's religious beliefs;
    d. which major religious group she or he belongs to (Jewish, Catholic, etc.);
  *e. the way in which a person's behavior is affected as a consequence of religiosity.

1207. (p. 477) (MD) Elizabeth J.'s son was killed in Vietnam. She had prayed often for his safety but upon learning of his death she understood that it was the Lord's punishment for the bad things she had done during her life. Such interpretations illustrate which of the roles of religiosity?
    a. security;
    b. death;
    c. social values;
  *d. crisis;
    e. confirming.

1208. (pp. 477-478) (LD) Among the personal or individual functions of religious commitment, the textbook discussed all of the following except which one?
    a. security;
    b. coping with crisis;
  *c. personality integration;
    d. coping with death;
    e. instilling social values.

1209. (p. 479) (MD) A woman prophet claimed to have received messages from another planet concerning a vast catastrophe that was about to happen to the earth. When her predictions failed to come true, she maintained that it was because God had decided to spare the earth. Her group of followers believed her "messages" on both counts. This illustrates the social-psychological principle that:

a. there are always people around who will believe anything;
b. the more outrageous the claim, the more likely it is that it will be believed;
c. beliefs will be shared to the degree that they lack credibility;
*d. beliefs gain credibility to the degree that they are shared;
e. such pronouncements are more likely to be trusted when made by a woman than by a man.

1210. (p. 480) (LD) In the theoretical formulation concerning religious groups advanced by Ernst Troeltsch, one "ideal type" was described as a large formal association with an elaborate status hierarchy plus highly institutionalized norms, roles, and sanctions. Troeltsch called this the:
*a. church;
b. sect;
c. cult;
d. congregation;
e. denomination.

1211. (p. 480) (LD) Among the following, which would provide the best example of "the church" in terms of Troeltsch's church-sect dichotomy?
a. the Shakers of nineteenth-century America;
*b. the Catholic Church of thirteenth-century Europe;
c. the Pilgrims who came to New England;
d. the Jesus movement among contemporary youth;
e. the early Christians of Roman times.

1212. (p. 480) (MD) In Troeltsch's theoretical formulation, a small group with voluntary membership emerges from the "church." It institutes its own form of worship and belief. Such a "sect" is usually based originally on:
a. a need to work out compromises with secular society that the "church" will not undertake;
b. the desire of its members to have more formality than the "church" provides;
*c. protest over church policy and a demand for reform;
d. charismatic leadership on the part of the head of the church;
e. the need to experience tighter bureaucratic control on the part of sect members.

1213. (p. 481) (MD) According to the definition given in the text, which of the following groups would be best characterized as a sect?
a. Catholic Church;
b. Baptists;
c. Unitarians;
d. Islam;
*e. Hasidic Jews.

1214. (p. 482) (MD) Which of the following would be closest to a denomination in Troeltsch's theory of religious organization?
a. sect;
*b. the church;
c. civil religion;
d. Pentecostalism;
e. the Jesus movement.

1215. (p. 482) (LD) Which of the following characterizes the "denomination" as a type of religious group?
a. accommodation to the secular world;
b. toleration for other similar groups;
c. membership generally acquired by birth;
d. conventionalized services;
*e. all of the above.

1216. (p. 483) (LD) The textbook states that religious leadership in
Pentecostal and Jesus groups tends to be:
a. women;
*b. authoritarian and charismatic;
c. upper-class individuals;
d. democratic and charismatic;
e. nonexistent.

1217. (p. 487) (MD) The social conditions that seem to favor the emergence
of religious innovators with special "messages" that they have claims
of divinity can best be described as:
a. periods of social unrest;
b. times when established systems of values begin to crumble;
c. mass migration, rapid urbanization, war, etc.;
d. periods of social tranquility when people are bored with
established religions;
*e. mainly during a, b, and c above.

1218. (p. 488) (LD) A messiah differs from a prophet in that a messiah:
a. is a charismatic leader while a prophet is not;
*b. claims to be a divinity while a prophet does not;
c. can become a member of a clergy while a prophet cannot;
d. does not experience revelations while a prophet does;
e. messiahs and prophets are essentially the same.

1219. (p. 488) (LD) Religious innovators who start sectarian groups or
claim to be in special communication with a deity, often possess
extraordinary powers or qualities in the eyes of their followers.
Sociologists refer to this as:
*a. charisma;
b. insight;
c. mysticism;
d. holiness;
e. magnetism.

1220. (p. 488) (LD) The main difference between the "messiah" and the
"prophet" as religious innovators is that the "messiah" (but not
the "prophet") claims which of the following?
a. charisma;
b. magnetism;
c. intelligence;
d. humility;
*e. divinity.

1221. (p. 488) (MD) A prophet claims to speak for a divinity in calling
for reform in the existing social or religious system. The best
example of a prophet is:

a. Pope Paul VI;
*b. Elijah Muhammad;
c. Father Divine;
d. all of the above;
e. only b and c.

1222. (pp. 488-489) (MD) Different patterns of social organization pre-
vail in the relationship between the clergy and ordinary church
members for Catholics as opposed to most Protestant denominations.
For Protestant clergy these differences often result in:
a. intensive attempts to clarify theological issues in sermons;
b. authoritarian positions on matters of religious ritual and
doctrine;
*c. emphasis on service roles, secular sermons, and adaptations to
needs of congregations;
d. a deemphasis on service roles and concern with secular issues;
e. a lack of concern with counseling activities and organizing
social activities.

1223. (p. 488) (MD) In terms of formal education, which of the following
groups uniformly require high educational attainment for their
clergy?
a. Catholics;
b. Jews;
c. Protestants;
d. all of the above;
*e. only a and b above.

1224. (p. 491) (LD) The most significant way in which religion aids in
the development and maintenance of social stability is:
a. by specifying specific meaningful rituals for such matters as
marriage, funerals, etc.;
b. by discouraging antigovernment activities, thereby reducing the
probability of social unrest;
*c. by defining sacred values and by prescribing behavioral codes
for their attainment which become the basis for mores;
d. by encouraging family life, thus increasing people's awareness
of responsibilities;
e. by providing a group of leaders (clergy) that serve as models
for ordinary people's behavior.

1225. (p. 491) (LD) Religion may contribute to social integration by:
a. defining important values for a society;
b. specifying systems of mores and other codes;
c. fostering the sharing of common beliefs;
d. aiding people in thinking of themselves as alike within a
given group;
*e. all of the above.

1226. (p. 489) (MD) Which of the following examples does not provide
support for the existence of a "civil religion" in the United States?
a. pledge of allegiance;
b. court oaths;
c. writing on currency;
d. the calendar;
*e. all of the above demonstrate a civil religion.

1227. (p. 491) (MD) According to the texbook, religion may promote social
       conflict by:
       a. providing the basis for wars and severe conflicts;
       b. setting up conflicts between important religious beliefs and
           civil law;
       c. fostering widespread exogamy in the society;
       d. all of the above;
      *e. only <u>a</u> and <u>b</u> above.

1228. (p. 491) (LD) Among the following, which is discussed in the text
       as a form of social conflict related to religion?
       a. persecution of religious minorities;
       b. clashes between major religious groups;
       c. disagreements over the relationship between church and state;
       d. conflicts between believers and nonbelievers;
      *e. all of the above.

1229. (p. 491) (MD) In the United States, social conflicts related to
       religion center around:
       a. tensions between major religious groups or between believers and
           nonbelievers;
       b. tensions between government and some religious groups;
       c. tensions between government and individuals claiming religious
           exemptions;
      *d. all of the above;
       e. only <u>a</u> and <u>c</u> above.

1230. (p. 492) (MD) Among religious groups in America, which has the
       membership with the highest educational and occupational attainment?
       a. Methodists;
      *b. Episcopalians;
       c. Catholics;
       d. Baptists (white);
       e. Lutherans.

1231. (p. 495) (MD) Distinctive styles of religious expression and partic-
       ipation that characterize different levels in the social class
       structure are closely related to:
       a. the different levels of human intelligence that characterize
           people from different classes;
       b. the different patterns of leadership that clergy exercise among
           high and low status groups;
      *c. the distinctive kinds of human needs that are generated at
           different levels of the social structure;
       d. the greater population density found among the poor;
       e. all of the above.

1232. (p. 496) (LD) Concerning the future of religion, a major change is
       toward <u>secularization</u>. This term implies that:
      *a. churches are defining their roles and missions in less "other-
           worldly" terms;
       b. religion is becoming less and less important in American society;
       c. people are going to church more for spiritual reasons than for
           social reasons;
       d. people are becoming increasingly cynical about true religious
           values and more interested in social appearances;
       e. churches are becoming more and more alike in their basic
           systems of theological belief.

1233. (p. 472) (LD) The Tools of Sociology, "Measuring Religiosity,"
discussed different levels of analysis of the concept of a "religious"
person. Among those discussed were:
   a. individual;
   b. institutional;
   c. societal;
*d. all of the above;
   e. <u>a</u> and <u>b</u> only.

1234. (p. 492) (MD) In the U.S., Protestants in general comprised about
what proportion of the total population as of 1972?
*a. 65 percent;
   b. 40 percent;
   c. 75 percent;
   d. 50 percent;
   e. 45 percent.

True-False

1235. (pp. 471-477) (MD) The overlap among different dimensions of
religiosity is very great. A person who is very religious in one
respect is likely to be very religious in other respects.
   a. true;
*b. false.

1236. (p. 471) (MD) According to a survey reported in the textbook,
Roman Catholics are generally more likely than Protestants to believe
in the divinity of Jesus.
*a. true;
   b. false.

1237. (pp. 473-474) (LD) After reviewing a number of examples of religious
rituals, the textbook concludes that there is much more uniformity
than variety among human beings in the kinds of rituals that are
practiced.
   a. true;
*b. false.

1238. (p. 476) (LD) The definition of "religious experience" used in the
textbook requires some sense of contact or communication with God or
some kind of divine essense.
*a. true;
   b. false.

1239. (p. 476) (LD) The religious experiences people have seem to have
little or nothing to do with the kinds of religious beliefs they
have.
   a. true;
*b. false.

1240. (p. 477) (LD) According to the text, believers who count on
religion to help them avert tragedies and disasters usually reject
their religion when it fails to work in that way.
   a. true;
*b. false.

1241. (pp. 477-478) (MD) The fact that belief in immortality is found in nearly all societies has led some scholars to suggest that such a belief may fulfill a basic social need.
*a. true;
 b. false.

1242. (p. 477) (LD) Social science research tends to show that individuals who are strongly linked through religious commitment to traditional norms and values gain a source of moral strength and behavioral stability.
*a. true;
 b. false.

1243. (p. 479) (MD) When Americans are grouped according to their religious affiliations, significant differences in behavior can be observed from one religious category to another.
*a. true;
 b. false.

1244. (p. 479) (LD) Experimental social psychology clearly indicates that beliefs gain credibility in proportion to the degree to which they are shared.
*a. true;
 b. false.

1245. (p. 480) (MD) One of the main differences between a church and a sect is the readiness of a sect to compromise.
 a. true;
*b. false.

1246. (p. 481) (LD) According to sociological theory, those sects which survive eventually are transformed into churches.
*a. true;
 b. false.

1247. (p. 481) (MD) Any religious group that persists over time and has a fairly large membership will have to cope with the same problems as a church.
*a. true;
 b. false.

1248. (pp. 481-483) (MD) One of the characteristic differences between sects and denominations is the extensive congregational participation in the latter.
 a. true;
*b. false.

1249. (p. 486) (MD) The early development of the Jesus Movement was a classic case of the growth of a denomination.
 a. true;
*b. false.

1250. (p. 488) (LD) Messiahs are religious innovators who frequently predict the coming of a millennium when the society or world will be transformed.

```
   *a.   true;
    b.   false.
```

1251. (p. 491) (MD) In the text, it was noted that the religious composi-
       tion of the United States was approximately two thirds Protestant,
       one fourth Catholic, and about three percent Jewish.
       *a.   true;
        b.   false.

1252. (p. 492) (LD) Religious affiliation is not merely a class phenome-
       non; all religious denominations and groups draw some members from
       each social stratum.
       *a.   true;
        b.   false.

1253. (p. 496) (MD) According to the text, the secularization of our
       society means that religion, in general, is declining in importance.
        a.   true;
       *b.   false.

1254. (p. 496) (LD) The textbook concludes that it will only be a short
       time before the challenge of science causes the more-or-less complete
       disappearance of religion in our society.
        a.   true;
       *b.   false.

Fill-In

1255. (p. 477) (LD) A form of experience in which individuals believe
       they have received a sacred message is called _____.

       revelation

1256. (p. 480) (LD) Because of its broad membership base and varied power
       alignments, a _____ must always be willing to compromise.

       church

1257. (p. 480) (MD) Membership in a _____ transcends all other
       allegiances in importance since it develops both informal and formal
       behavior codes that members are expected to follow.

       sect

1258. (p. 488) (LD) A religious innovator who claims to speak for a
       divinity and urges reform in the existing social or religious system
       is called a _____.

       prophet

1259. (p. 488) (LD) A _____ _____ seems most likely to
       emerge in times of social unrest.

       religious innovator

1260. (p. 496) (MD) It was noted in the text that our society and
       churches have become increasingly _____, less other-worldly.

       secular

Matching

1261. (pp. 471-477) (LD)
       belief   may differ sharply from
                                             theological tenets
       ritual   symbolizing some aspect of a
                                             faith
       experience   strongly shaped by social and
                                             cultural background
       revelation   receiving a sacred "message"
       knowledge   history and traditions of
                                             faith

1262. (pp. 480-488) (LD)
       universal church   found in socially homogeneous
                                             societies
       messiah   coming of millennium
       denomination   emotional conversions are rare
       sect   spontaneous commitment
       prophet   reform leadership

1263. (pp. 480-483) (MD)
       sect   limited wealth
       denomination   members born into group
       sect   extensive congregational
                                             participation
       denomination   endorses prevailing culture
                                             and organization
       denomination   accepts other religious groups

1264. (pp. 492-496) (MD)
       industrial and scientific   churches becoming less other-
         progress   worldly
       qualitative approach to religion   quality of religious experience
         and social class
       civil religion   national symbols and rituals
       adaptation   new religious behavior

Short Essay

1265. (pp. 471-477) (LD) Name and briefly discuss the dimensions of
       religiosity.

       Major points: belief, ritual, experience, and knowledge.

1266. (pp. 487-489) (MD) Discuss briefly the two types of religious
       leaders and their styles of leadership.

       Major points: religious innovator (prophet or messiah) and the
       clergy.

1267. (pp. 492-495) (MD) Name and briefly discuss the two approaches to
       the study of religion and social class.

       Major points: quantitative and qualitative approaches.

1268. (pp. 495-496) (LD) Discuss two ways in which American churches are
       changing or may change in the future.

Major points: may include secularization, adaptation, and the challenge of science.

Broad Essay

1269.   (pp. 471-478) (LD) Review the main individual "functions" of religion and show how they are related to the various dimensions of religiosity.

Major points: functions: security, crises, death, social values; dimensions: belief, ritual, experience, revelation.

1270.   (pp. 480-483) (MD) Compare and contrast a sect and a denomination, giving particular attention to such characteristics as size, relationship with other religious groups, clergy, doctrines, membership requirements, relationship with secular world, and the social class of members.

Major points: sects are usually small, lower-class, relatively poor groups which are "at war" with the secular world and reject other religious groups; denominations are large, middle-class groups with extensive wealth which endorse the prevailing culture and accept other denominations.

1271.   (p. 491) (MD) Explain why some social scientists believe that religion functions primarily to promote social integration in most societies.

Major points: religion provides a basis for system of mores, which is closely related to and dependent upon law; sharing of common beliefs is in itself integrating.

1272.   (pp. 495-496) (LD) Discuss the future of religion in our society. In what ways is it changing and what new forms might it take in the future?

Major points: secularization, adaptation, challenge of science.

CHAPTER 17.   The Political Institution

Multiple Choice

1273.   (p. 498) (LD) For Weber, the legitimacy of the state lies in:
   *a.   its claim to the legitimate use of force;
   b.   free elections;
   c.   traditional authority;
   d.   its constitution;
   e.   all of the above.

1274.   (p. 499) (LD) Following Max Weber, the text defines power as:
   a.   the possession of a dynamic personality;
   b.   the right to rule provided by constitutional authority;
   *c.   the ability to make and implement decisions;
   d.   the possession of the economic means to do what one wishes;
   e.   the degree of force that one can ultimately command.

1275. (p. 499) (LD) According to Weber, political power is first and foremost the kind of power exercised by:
    a. employers;
    b. military officers;
    c. bankers;
    *d. the state;
    e. the bourgeoisie generally.

1276. (p. 499) (MD) A "crisis of legitimacy" occurs in a political system under which of the following conditions?
    a. when it is inefficient in accomplishing the tasks of government;
    b. when it fails to provide for popular participation in decision-making;
    c. when it places military goals above public welfare;
    *d. when its values are rejected by significant segments of its population;
    e. under any of the above conditions.

1277. (p. 500) (LD) The process of establishing institutionalized norms defining a situation as right and proper concerning power relations (e.g., the right of the police to protect private property) is called:
    a. politicization;
    b. regularization;
    c. normalization;
    *d. legitimization;
    e. subordination.

1278. (p. 500) (LD) In political sociology, power based on the illegitimate use or threat of force is called:
    a. aggression;
    b. a dictatorship;
    *c. coercion;
    d. a revolution;
    e. nonsanctioned.

1279. (p. 500) (MD) The main difference between authority and coercion in political sociology is the factor of:
    a. power;
    *b. legitimacy;
    c. charisma;
    d. persuasion;
    e. organization.

1280. (p. 500) (MD) The text suggests that the ultimate basis of a social order may rest upon the fact that members of a society share a body of beliefs, values, and sentiments. In other words, in the last analysis, the basis of legitimacy is:
    a. power;
    b. authority;
    *c. consensus;
    d. sanctions;
    e. force.

1281. (p. 500) (LD) According to the text, the meaning of the term consensus is most clearly approximated by which of the following?

*a.   generally shared norms concerning values, beliefs, and senti-
      ments;
 b.   general agreement on a specific political candidate;
 c.   the results of a public opinion poll showing that people
      generally favor a particular policy;
 d.   the absence of political conflict in a system, leading to a
      period of stability;
 e.   widespread satisfaction with a given political situation.

1282.   (p. 501) (MD) Among the Mogo (a primitive society) the chief holds
        his power because the people believe that his legitimization is
        almost sacred, having been handed down from the past. Weber would
        refer to this type of authority as:
        a.   primitive;
        b.   classical;
        c.   historical;
        d.   transitional;
       *e.   traditional.

1283.   (p. 502) (LD) Which of the following characteristics is generally
        associated with a group with the charismatic type of authority as
        discussed in the text?
        a.   has clear tests for competency for leaders;
       *b.   lacks stable social organization;
        c.   does not conflict with tradition and routine;
        d.   has strongly institutionalized norms and roles;
        e.   all of the above.

1284.   (p. 502) (MD) Father Divine was a well-known leader among black
        Americans some years ago. His followers believed him to be a person
        of special spiritual significance. The type of authority he exer-
        cised over his organization would have been classified by Weber as:
        a.   spiritual;
       *b.   charismatic;
        c.   divine;
        d.   dynamic;
        e.   irrational.

1285.   (p. 502) (LD) Among the following groups, which is most likely to
        base its legitimate exercise of power upon a legal-rational type of
        authority?
        a.   a family;
        b.   a peer group;
        c.   a social movement;
        d.   a primitive tribe;
       *e.   a federal agency.

1286.   (p. 502) (LD) Which of the following characterizes influence in
        the political process (as discussed in the text)?
        a.   it is less personal in nature than is authority;
        b.   it has little to do with such factors as personal charm,
             wealth, or persuasiveness;
        c.   it is identical with authority according to most political
             sociologists;
       *d.   it represents the sum of all the resources an individual can
             bring to bear on a decision-making process;

e.   all of the above.

1287.   (p. 504) (MD)   The text cites such organizations as the American
Medical Association, the National Association of Electrical Companies, the Brotherhood of Teamsters, etc., that employ professional
specialists to make personal contacts with legislators to promote
the goals of their respective groups.   In the political influence
process this activity is called:
a.   buttonholing;
b.   jawboning;
c.   earbending;
d.   pressuring;
*e.   lobbying.

1288.   (p. 504) (LD)   Although the practice of lobbying occurs all around
the political system, it is most commonly and properly the activity
of which of the following kinds of political entities?
a.   political parties;
*b.   interest groups;
c.   vested interests;
d.   political bosses;
e.   city councils.

1289.   (p. 507) (LD)   The ethnocentric belief that one's nation is better
than any other is called:
a.   patriotism;
*b.   nationalism;
c.   superiority;
d.   absolutism;
e.   preeminence.

1290.   (pp. 508-509) (MD)   A democratic political system is made "workable"
by:
a.   a numerous middle class;
b.   compatible political traditions;
c.   a relatively high level of economic development;
d.   voluntary associations independent of the state;
*e.   all of the above.

1291.   (p. 509) (MD)   A study by Lipset of the social conditions of forty-
eight politically stable and unstable countries showed that a basic
factor leading to democracy and stability was:
a.   favorable climate;
*b.   economic development;
c.   English traditions;
d.   racial harmony;
e.   charismatic leadership.

1292.   (p. 509) (MD)   Voluntary associations are valuable to democracies
because they serve several important needs.   These include all of
the following except:
a.   political training;
b.   communication;
*c.   socialization into traditional ideas;
d.   political opposition;
e.   stimulating political activity.

1293. (p. 512) (MD) Available evidence suggests that the council-manager type of local government is more likely to be found in cities with:
   a. medium-to-high conflict levels;
   *b. high proportions of middle-class business and professional people;
   c. alienated business and professional people;
   d. a and c only;
   e. none of the above.

1294. (p. 512) (MD) Evidence from recent studies of various systems of community government has indicated which of the following?
   *a. conflict levels are lower in cities with the council-manager form of government than in cities with the traditional two-party system;
   b. business and professional groups prefer the traditional two-party approach to local government;
   c. political conflict is maximized in communities with a high proportion of middle-class citizens;
   d. pluralism--that is, competition for power by various segments of the population--actually reduces conflict in political decision-making;
   e. only a and d are correct.

1295. (p. 512) (MD) Which of the following hypotheses has had the most time and attention devoted to it (according to the text)?
   a. prospects for revolution in America;
   b. the implications of professional leadership in community power;
   c. the differences between authority and influence in community power;
   d. military control of American political structures;
   *e. business control of the community.

1296. (p. 513) (LD) Studies on the influence of people in local community politics have produced which of the following unequivocal facts?
   a. the dominance of business people in positions of political power indicates a coordinated strategy on their part to maintain control;
   b. business people rarely appear on opposing factions in local politics;
   c. business people are actually becoming less and less influential in local politics each year;
   *d. the business sector of the community produces most of the community leaders;
   e. professional rather than business people have always been the most influential in local politics.

1297. (p. 513) (LD) Sociological research in numerous American cities aimed at discovering the prevailing type of power structure has shown that community power is:
   a. increasingly centralized with political power in the hands of a few people;
   *b. becoming less centralized;
   c. based on monolithic control with a single dominant person in charge;

d. based on oligarchic control with power in the hands of a clique;
e. none of the above.

1298. (p. 514) (LD) In Tools of Sociology, "Measuring Community Power," the authors make the point that the simplest and most objective approach for measuring community power is the:
*a. positional approach;
b. reputational approach;
c. decision-making approach;
d. influential approach;
e. issues approach.

1299. (p. 514) (MD) Floyd Hunter pioneered which of the following approaches to the measurement of community power?
a. decision-making;
*b. reputational;
c. positional;
d. issues;
e. business elite.

1300. (p. 515) (LD) In the Tools of Sociology section on political power, the authors of the textbook explain various approaches to the study of community power, but they give an especially detailed example of which of the following approaches?
a. positional;
b. reputational;
c. power elite;
*d. issues;
e. consensus.

1301. (p. 516) (MD) According to the study (by Walton) reported on in the textbook, a decentralization of power in modern communities has resulted from which of the following factors?
a. the continual movement toward absentee-owned industry;
b. the tendency of local governments to become more involved with state and federal governments;
c. the tendency for voluntary and professional groups within communities to have outside ties;
d. only b and c;
*e. a, b, and c.

1302. (p. 516) (LD) In spite of the concept of "separation of powers" in the United States Constitution, which of the following branches of government has become the most powerful?
*a. executive;
b. legislative;
c. judicial;
d. military;
e. scientific.

1303. (p. 520) (MD) In discussing the role of the legislator as "broker" the text notes that this term describes the legislator's relationship as a mediator between:
a. the executive and legislature itself;
b. the business world and the local government;
c. the political party and the legislature;

*d. the local citizens to whom the legislator is responsible and
    the executive;
 e. the power elite and the ordinary citizen.

1304. (pp. 521-523) (MD) The power structure of the American society
has been studied by such writers as G. William Domhoff, C. Wright
Mills, and Arnold Rose. Concerning their conclusions, it can be
said that:
 a. the evidence consistently supports the conclusion that Americans
    are dominated by a power elite of military, industrial, and
    political figures;
 b. the evidence strongly rejects the conclusion that a power elite
    dominates American life;
 c. there is a power elite, but they are of European rather than
    American origin;
 d. the actual power in this country is in the hands of one particu-
    lar religious group;
*e. there is no clear evidence of an American "power elite" who
    dominate the majority.

1305. (p. 523) (LD) According to the text, which of the following institutions seems to be the most influential in forming children's
political attitudes?
 a. church;
 b. mass media;
 c. school;
 d. peer group;
*e. family.

1306. (pp. 523-526) (LD) The term political socialization, as discussed
in the textbook, refers mainly to which of the following?
*a. the instilling and training of political attitudes in children;
 b. the social interaction that takes place at political meetings;
 c. the use of the mass media for propaganda purposes;
 d. the pulling together of diverse elements into an integrated
    political party;
 e. convincing members of one political party to convert to the
    other's views.

1307. (pp. 523-524) (LD) Political socialization in the United States is
strongly influenced by:
 a. the political traditions of one's family;
 b. the political ideas taught in school;
 c. the political views popular in one's ethnic group;
 d. the political subculture prevalent in one's social class;
*e. all of the above.

1308. (p. 524) (MD) The political values which are transmitted to
children as they grow up are likely to come mainly from which of
the following cultural sources?
 a. religion;
 b. school;
 c. father's occupation;
 d. college student subculture;
*e. social class.

1309. (pp. 524-526) (MD) Voter turnout figures for most industrial
democracies range between 70 and 90 percent. By comparison, the
United States can be said to be:
a. relatively enthusiastic with turnout rates uniformly above 90
percent in recent years;
b. relatively similar with an average turnout rate of approximately
80 percent;
c. dreadfully apathetic with turnout rates for national elections
averaging only about 30 percent;
d. extremely variable, with turnout rates for national elections
ranging from 10 to 95 percent;
*e. relatively apathetic with only about 60 to 70 percent of
qualified voters actually going to the polls.

1310. (p. 524) (MD) Which of the following conclusions was reached
regarding political participation in the United States?
a. apathy is greatest among the middle and upper classes;
b. education has no effect on political participation;
c. voter turnout among blacks has increased due to power politics
of the Black Power Movement;
*d. participation is negatively (inversely) related to deprivation
and discrimination;
e. participation is not related to these social variables.

True-False

1311. (pp. 499-500) (LD) According to the textbook, consensus is important
in a democratic system, but it is unimportant in a totalitarian one.
a. true;
*b. false.

1312. (p. 500) (LD) Most revolutions are spontaneous mass uprisings
against unpopular regimes.
a. true;
*b. false.

1313. (p. 500) (LD) History has taught us that revolutions have not
occurred in the Western hemisphere since the American Revolution.
a. true;
*b. false.

1314. (p. 501) (MD) The oldest form of power known to humans is traditional authority, in which legitimization has been handed down
from the past.
*a. true;
b. false.

1315. (p. 502) (LD) Charismatic leaders' claim to legitimacy lies
primarily in their own inner perception of personal power.
*a. true;
b. false.

1316. (p. 502) (MD) By its very nature, charismatic authority is transi-
tional and must eventually evolve into either of the other two
kinds of authority.

*a. true;
 b. false.

1317. (p. 502) (LD) In the legal-rational system of authority, limits are
       set upon the power of leaders by the carefully defined bureaucratic
       roles they occupy.
       *a. true;
        b. false.

1318. (p. 502) (MD) Influence is more of an individual phenomenon than
       authority since it does not inhere in the office or position as
       authority does.
       *a. true;
        b. false.

1319. (p. 503) (LD) When persons in authority lack personal influence,
       outsiders may be expected to move in to fill the gap.
       *a. true;
        b. false.

1320. (p. 503) (LD) Although urban political party "machines" were once
       very powerful in American cities, they have now largely disappeared
       in most cities.
       *a. true;
        b. false.

1321. (p. 509) (MD) According to the textbook, it is one of the paradoxes
       of political organization that totally autonomous communities tend
       to be more competitive and to provide more individual freedom for
       their members than do communities that are more dependent on a
       central government.
        a. true;
       *b. false.

1322. (p. 510) (LD) The textbook suggests that people are likely to
       resort to breaking laws to bring about change if they perceive that
       the "system" provides them no real way to achieve their desired
       goals by acceptable means.
       *a. true;
        b. false.

1323. (pp. 511-515) (MD) Political sociologists, according to the text-
       book, are not interested in all aspects of the political decision-
       making process so much as in those aspects dealing with the formal
       political structures.
        a. true;
       *b. false.

1324. (p. 512) (MD) The authors of the textbook conclude that the trend
       toward council-manager municipal government is consistent with
       democratic processes.
        a. true;
       *b. false.

1325. (p. 512) (LD) Considerable evidence suggests that a community's
       business sector produces most of the political decision-makers.

*a. true;
b. false.

1326. (p. 513) (MD) Recent studies examining the patterns of power structures in American cities have produced evidence that power has become less centralized.
*a. true;
b. false.

1327. (pp. 512-513) (MD) The general national tendency for issues to take on political overtones has begun to spread to the local community level, where partisan politics are more important than ever.
a. true;
*b. false.

1328. (p. 513) (LD) The most important finding that can be generalized from all the recent studies on community power (according to the text) is that no single pyramid of power has been uncovered in any American city.
*a. true;
b. false.

1329. (p. 519) (LD) The textbook reports on research that demonstrates the political power of the military is equal to that of elected officials.
a. true;
*b. false.

1330. (p. 522) (LD) According to one major study of power elites reported in the textbook (Rose), there are a number of power structures in American society, and no unified elite is in control of all or any of them.
*a. true;
b. false.

1331. (p. 523) (LD) The ethnic factor is becoming less important in American politics.
a. true;
*b. false.

1332. (p. 526) (MD) The textbook reports that political apathy is greatest among the middle and upper classes who see no reason to change a system that they benefit from.
a. true;
*b. false.

1333. (p. 527) (MD) The authors of the textbook conclude from research on political participation that the consensus basis for American democracy may be corroding.
*a. true;
b. false.

1334. (p. 526) (LD) Generally speaking, political participation in the U.S. is directly correlated with social class.

*a. true;
b. false.

1335. (p. 506) (MD) Unlike communism, fascism is characterized by free
enterprise capitalism and the right to individual and corporate
profit.
*a. true;
b. false.

1336. (p. 506) (MD) Democracy has no place in a communist society, according to the textbook.
a. true;
*b. false.

1337. (p. 515) (MD) The results of one study of community power reported
at length in the textbook (Dahl's on New Haven) suggest that in
most American communities there is little overlap among leaders or
influentials from issue to issue.
*a. true;
b. false.

Fill-In

1338. (p. 502) (MD) _____ authority is usually in conflict with
routine.

Charismatic

1339. (p. 502) (LD) _____ may be derived from a position of
authority, but it may also be derived from personal charm, wealth,
etc.

Influence

1340. (p. 504) (MD) The practice of lobbying is most properly and commonly
the activity of a _____ group.

pressure

1341. (p. 512) (MD) The deemphasis of political conflict in local governments has resulted in a _____ _____ system of
government.

council-manager

1342. (p. 523) (LD) The primary agent of political socialization is the

_____.

family

1343. (p. 514) (LD) The _____ approach to the study of community
power assumes the power structure is reflected in the formal systems
of authority.

positional

Matching

1344. (pp. 499-502) (LD)

rests on system of authority	legitimate power
rests on threat or use of force	coercive power
in conflict with routine	charismatic authority
obligation to obey is based upon "the rule of the law"	legal-rational authority
task of leaders is to find precedents to justify any novelty	traditional authority

1345. (pp. 502-504) (MD)

inhering more in individual	influence
inhering more in office	authority
exerts influence without being a political party	interest group
lacks stable social organization	charismatic authority
belief that political institutions are most appropriate	legitimacy

1346. (pp. 505-513) (MD)

centralized authority	nation-state
ethnocentrism	nationalism
prevailing community power pattern	decentralized
council-manager system of government	deemphasis of political conflict
minimum of representation for working classes and minorities	council-manager system of government

1347. (pp. 514-526) (LD)

power structure is reflected in the formal systems of authority	positional approach
reputation for influence implies some degree of actual power	reputational approach
power inheres in those persons who can successfully carry through or block action	issues approach
works best for middle and upper classes	political socialization
influential in forming political attitudes	family

Short Essay

1348. (pp. 501-502) (LD) Briefly describe the three types of authority delineated by Weber.

Major points: traditional, charismatic, and legal-rational.

1349. (pp. 501-503) (MD) Discuss the difference between authority and influence.

Major points: authority: right to make or implement decisions that have been made through acceptable channels; influence: all the resources one can bring to bear in a decision-making situation to ensure the outcome one wants; it inheres in the individual more than the office.

1350. (pp. 508-510) (MD) Discuss two of the prerequisites for a democratic system as given in the text.

Major points: class structure, political traditions, and voluntary
associations.

1351. (pp. 514-515) (LD) Briefly describe two of the approaches to the
study of community power.

Major points: positional, reputational, and/or issues approaches.

Broad Essay

1352. (pp. 499-502) (MD) Discuss the concepts of legitimacy and authority.
How does authority differ from power? Name and discuss the different types of authority as delineated by Weber.

Major points: legitimacy: political system can be considered
legitimate if it is able to maintain the belief that the existing
political institutions are the most appropriate ones for the
society; authority: right to make or implement decisions that
have been made through acceptable structural channels; three types
of authority are charismatic, traditional, and legal-rational;
power: probability that one actor within a relationship will be
in a position to carry out his or her will despite resistance.

1353. (pp. 505-510) (LD) Define and explain the principle of democracy,
the conditions necessary for its development, and the role of
conflict in democracies.

Major points: Western democracy is essentially the legitimate
existence of effective opposition to those in power and in principle
does not imply a particular economic system; factors important to
its development include the existence of a class structure dominated
by the middle class, a relatively high level of economic development, political traditions favoring democracy, and independent
voluntary associations; opposition and political conflict are
legitimate.

1354. (pp. 511-516) (MD) Discuss the characteristics of present-day power
structures at the community level.

Major points: diffusion of community power, deemphasis of political
conflict, politics as an avenue to influence, leadership comes from
business sector.

1355. (pp. 523-527) (LD) Discuss what factors are most influential in the
political socialization of children. Why is political socialization
becoming more problematic in the U.S.?

Major points: family, ethnicity, and class are the most influential;
political socialization is no longer uniform because of the size
and complexity of our society; this could bring into question the
legitimacy of our government.

CHAPTER 18. The Economic Institution

Multiple Choice

1356. (p. 528) (MD) The consequential development of the Western economic
       institution is said to extend back to:
       *a. the Middle Ages;
        b. Roman times or even earlier;
        c. the earliest colonization of the New World;
        d. the American Civil War;
        e. the beginning of the 1800s.

1357. (p. 529) (LD) The medieval organization that controlled production
       of goods was the:
        a. home factory;
        b. royal committee;
        c. producer's union;
       *d. craft guild;
        e. town council.

1358. (p. 529) (LD) The system of production in which families working in
       their homes produced work for a given merchant, after receiving raw
       materials, was called the:
        a. domestic system;
        b. putting-out system;
        c. cottage-industry system;
       *d. all of the above;
        e. none of the above.

1359. (p. 529) (MD) The production system inherent in the operations of
       craft guilds was gradually displaced when control over their produc-
       tion came into the hands of:
        a. the nobility;
        b. early factory owners;
        c. the workers themselves;
        d. unscrupulous bankers;
       *e. merchants or middlemen.

1360. (p. 529) (MD) The preindustrial domestic or "putting-out" system
       of production was based upon which of the following features?
        a. middlemen;
        b. cottage industry;
        c. strong guilds;
        d. all of the above;
       *e. only a and b.

1361. (p. 531) (MD) The basis of industrial capitalism--investments in
       land, buildings, machines, raw materials, and labor--was called:
        a. fluid capital;
        b. real capital;
        c. monetary capital;
       *d. fixed capital;
        e. common capital.

1362. (pp. 531-532) (LD) The main features of the "factory system" as
it developed during the early nineteenth century did <u>not</u> include
which one of the following features?
  a. investment capital;
 *b. the "putting-out" system;
  c. steam-powered machines;
  d. a pool of "free" labor;
  e. "shop" production.

1363. (p. 531) (LD) The development of the so-called factory town was
originally made possible by which of the following technological
developments?
  a. improved transportation;
  b. the rise of mechanical technology;
  c. political democracy;
 *d. controlled steam power;
  e. mass media advertising.

1364. (p. 531) (MD) Which of the following factors contributed substantially to the availability of a large supply of labor in Britain's
early factory system?
  a. heavy immigration of poor people from the colonies;
  b. the farm-to-city movement generated by the new technology;
 *c. new laws evicting the rural poor from the land;
  d. the upheaval of traditional values caused by the Napoleonic Wars;
  e. all of the above.

1365. (p. 532) (MD) The concept of the "corporation," including multiple
ownership and risk-taking plus nonpersonal responsibility, came
into popularity:
 *a. during the growth of industrial capitalism in the nineteenth
      century;
  b. during the classic Roman period;
  c. in the early decades of the twentieth century;
  d. about the time of Columbus' discovery of the New World;
  e. during the development of the craft guilds of the Middle Ages.

1366. (p. 532) (MD) During the rise of industrialism in the United States,
corporations grew greatly in size, number, and economic power. So
much public concern resulted from their attempts to control trade
that federal legislation was passed to prevent combinations of
corporations from "restraint of trade." This was the famous:
 *a. Sherman Antitrust Act of 1890;
  b. Thirty-Second Amendment to the Constitution;
  c. Taft-Hartley Law of 1901;
  d. Anti-Corporation Law of 1934;
  e. Smoot-Hawley Restriction Law of 1834.

1367. (p. 532) (LD) Among the advantages to individual investors of
participating as stockholders in a corporation is:
  a. they can usually control the corporation because ownership
      implies control;
  b. they will always make some kind of profit;
  c. they have their investment insured by the government;
  d. the risk is very low because while private businesses fail,
      corporations do not;

*e. if the corporation fails, their personal property is
protected.

1368. (p. 533) (LD) A very large part of the stock of American corporations is owned by:
a. a dozen wealthy families;
b. the federal government;
c. the managers of those corporations;
d. people on relief;
*e. other organizations (churches, universities, etc.).

1369. (p. 533) (LD) Manufacturing facilities (plants, factories, etc.)
in the United States are owned less and less by individuals and
more and more by corporations of stockholders. In fact, approximately half of the manufacturing facilities of our country are owned
by the following number of corporations:
a. 10;
b. 875;
c. 293;
d. 1000;
*e. 100.

1370. (p. 533) (LD) A large corporation or conglomerate with substantial
business operations in at least six countries is called:
a. a super-industry;
*b. a multinational corporation;
c. an international corporation;
d. a cross-cultural conglomerate;
e. a corporation-pact.

1371. (p. 533) (MD) The majority of multinational corporations are owned
by:
*a. Americans;
b. British;
c. Russians;
d. Arabs;
e. N.A.T.O.

1372. (p. 536) (LD) The profit that accrues to a product after all costs
have been accounted for is the:
a. net profit;
b. clear profit;
c. fixed capital;
*d. surplus value;
e. investment capital.

1373. (p. 536) (MD) Max Weber identified the prerequisites of a capital-
istic system. They include all of the following except:
*a. democratic processes;
b. a system of law;
c. double-entry bookkeeping;
d. a "free" labor force;
e. a "free" market.

1374. (p. 536) (MD) According to Wilensky and Lebeaux, the ideology of
American capitalism includes the belief that:

a. failure is a sign of moral weakness;
b. rewards should be equally distributed;
c. success comes from competition;
d. all of the above;
*e. a and c only.

1375. (p. 538) (MD) The organizational structure of an industrial
corporation, in a formal sense, would illustrate most closely the
theoretical concepts of:
*a. Max Weber;
b. Herbert Spencer;
c. Auguste Comte;
d. Charles Cooley;
e. Louis Wirth.

1376. (pp. 538-540) (LD) Among the following, which was not discussed in
the text as a major segment of organization in modern corporate
industry?
a. line and staff;
b. middle management;
c. chief executive;
*d. secretaries and clerks;
e. line supervision.

1377. (pp. 538-539) (LD) In a manufacturing corporation, the items that
are actually assembled by workers are the product and responsibility
of:
a. staff divisions;
*b. line divisions;
c. middle managers;
d. design departments;
e. research groups.

1378. (pp. 538-539) (MD) Which of the following levels of industrial
bureaucracy is likely to feature the greatest complexity and frustration, according to the textbook?
a. board of directors;
b. top management;
*c. middle management;
d. supervisors;
e. office managers.

1379. (pp. 539-540) (MD) The kinds of informal conflicts and tensions
in industry which the textbook discusses include which of the
following?
a. staff vs. line;
b. vice-president vs. vice-president;
c. top management vs. middle management;
*d. all of the above;
e. only a and c.

1380. (pp. 539-540) (LD) The problem of the "power struggle" and its
consequences was discussed in the textbook mainly in connection
with which of the following roles in the industrial bureaucracy?
*a. vice-president;
b. board of directors;

c. foreman;
d. staff officer;
e. shop steward.

1381. (p. 541) (LD) Among American workers in all segments of the labor
force (including agricultural workers), which of the following most
closely approximates the percentage who belong to a labor union?
a. about one third;
b. slightly over one half;
*c. about one fifth;
d. nearly three fourths;
e. about ninety percent.

1382. (p. 542) (MD) Labor unions are in a formal sense bureaucratic
associations. However, the text maintains that their formal structure is more democratic than that of other associations because:
a. top union leaders insist upon deciding things by democratic
processes;
b. workers are more in tune with democratic procedures than those
who manage companies;
c. unions are based upon a truly democratic set of principles that
are not found in other groups;
*d. these associations have as a major goal the collective benefit
of their members;
e. the federal government requires that all unions organize themselves into a two-party system.

1383. (p. 542) (LD) The union official with whom workers have the most
frequent and regular day-to-day contact is called the:
a. straw boss;
b. business agent;
c. foreman;
d. secretary-treasurer;
*e. steward.

1384. (p. 544) (MD) Sociological research into work groups, for all
intents and purposes, began with Elton Mayo's investigations in the
Western Electric factory at Hawthorne (near Chicago):
a. in the late 1890s;
b. just prior to World War I (about 1910);
c. during the Great Depression of the 1930s;
d. during World War II in the 1940s;
*e. during the late 1920s.

1385. (pp. 544-545) (LD) An early sociological study of workers (by Mayo
at Western Electric) found that worker output was determined largely
by which of the following?
a. management quotas;
b. worker morale;
*c. work-group norms and pressures;
d. physical environment;
e. boredom and fatigue factors.

1386. (p. 545) (MD) The net result of the research done in the "human
relations era" has been to suggest that which of the following
factors is (are) usually important work motivation for industrial
workers?

a. money;
b. high morale;
c. work-group values and norms;
d. all of the above;
*e. only a and c.

1387. (p. 546) (MD) The term occupation implies a specialized role that is defined in rather specific terms within the context of a labor market. As such, occupations:
a. characterize any large bureaucratic group;
b. predate the industrial society by many centuries;
c. are found rather widely in primitive societies;
*d. are found mainly in industrial societies;
e. have been an important part of all societies during all historical periods.

1388. (p. 547) (LD) Tools of Sociology, "Measuring the Labor Force," explains that official information on employment is assembled and made public by:
a. the Unemployment Bureau of the FBI;
b. the major labor unions in the U.S.;
c. the Congress;
*d. the U.S. Bureau of Labor Statistics;
e. the Office of Economic Opportunity (of the Commerce Department).

1389. (p. 547) (MD) According to Tools of Sociology, "Measuring the Labor Force," which of the following is (are) requirement(s) for being classified as unemployed in the Current Population Survey?
a. person is between the ages of 14 and 65;
b. work was sought during the previous week;
c. person must live in household;
*d. all of the above;
e. there is no "unemployed" classification.

1390. (p. 548) (MD) Occupational choices, according to the text, are not "free rational choices limited only by natural ability." In fact, they are limited by all except which one of the following?
*a. moral and ethical correlates of specific jobs;
b. youthful ignorance of occupational roles;
c. lack of knowledge about job opportunities;
d. the range of available role models;
e. cultural values and reference groups.

1391. (p. 548) (LD) Adolescent vocational aspirations:
*a. generally far exceed what the majority of youth will eventually achieve;
b. are usually aimed at blue-collar jobs;
c. are closely related to the jobs eventually taken;
d. are seldom aimed toward professional and managerial roles;
e. seldom exceed eventual occupational choice, but often are at a lower level.

1392. (pp. 549-550) (MD) In which of the following ways have the occupational roles of men and women become more similar?
a. earning potential;
b. job opportunities;

c. importance of work;
*d. all of the above;
e. their roles are not becoming more similar.

1393. (p. 551) (LD) Karl Marx maintained that the industrial workers are in jobs that are meaningless to them and that they are also relatively powerless to change routines of work. This situation is termed:
a. brainwashing;
b. frustration;
c. proletariat;
*d. alienation;
e. capitalism.

1394. (p. 552) (LD) Which of the following is not a dimension of alienation in Blauner's research?
a. meaninglessness;
b. self-estrangement;
c. powerlessness;
d. social alienation;
*e. all of the above were dimensions.

1395. (p. 552) (MD) In Blauner's research on industrial workers, the dimension of alienation which is defined as the inability to see how one's task contributes to the production process is called:
a. powerlessness;
*b. meaninglessness;
c. social alienation;
d. self-estrangement;
e. contributive failure.

1396. (pp. 553-556) (MD) According to recent research done on certain forms of alienation among American workers, which of the following findings was reported in the textbook?
a. white-collar workers are more likely to be alienated than blue-collar workers;
b. alienation rates are about the same for blue- and white-collar workers;
c. there was no evidence of alienation found among American workers;
*d. blue-collar workers are more likely to be alienated than white-collar workers;
e. alienation simply does not exist among American workers, although they often feel powerless and find their work meaningless.

1397. (p. 557) (LD) Unemployment rates are related to:
a. race;
b. sex;
c. age;
*d. all of the above;
e. a and b only.

1398. (pp. 557-558) (LD) A significant dimension of the impact of unemployment on individuals in American society is:
a. its economic implications;
b. the challenge it poses to their self-image;
c. its implications for their place and worth in the social structure;

    d. it could threaten the structure of society;
*e. all of the above.

1399. (p. 558) (MD) In American society the "ethic of work" defines the
    unemployed person as:
    a. an unfortunate victim of impersonal economic factors;
    b. part of the lower class;
*c. a "moral" failure;
    d. an economic problem, but nothing else;
    e. either <u>a</u> or <u>b</u> above, depending upon region of country.

True-False

1400. (p. 529) (LD) Generally speaking, the medieval craft guilds
    welcomed the development of "cottage industries" and tried to inte-
    grate them into the system.
    a. true;
*b. false.

1401. (p. 530) (LD) The rise of the factory system in Britain represented
    the emergence of an entirely new kind of relationship between capital,
    labor, and technology.
*a. true;
    b. false.

1402. (p. 531) (LD) The factory system could not have come into existence
    without a large labor pool.
*a. true;
    b. false.

1403. (p. 532) (MD) Although the idea of a corporation had been known in
    Europe for a long time, the rise of corporations on a large scale
    did not come into existence until well after the start of the
    factory system.
*a. true;
    b. false.

1404. (pp. 532-533) (LD) The ownership of large modern corporations has
    become more and more separated from the control of them.
*a. true;
    b. false.

1405. (p. 533) (MD) The authors of the text suggèst that, while the
    <u>ownership</u> of corporations may be spreading to more and more people,
    the control of the corporations is apparently falling into <u>fewer</u>
    hands.
*a. true;
    b. false.

1406. (p. 536) (LD) The ideology of American capitalism holds that
    unequal rewards should be given for unequal talents.
*a. true;
    b. false.

1407. (p. 537) (MD) The authors of the text conclude that the ideology of
    American capitalism is a good reflection of the reality of economic
    life.

a. true;
*b. false.

1408. (p. 539) (LD) The personal, authoritative, "tycoon" style of leadership for corporation presidents seems to be less common today than earlier in the history of industry.
*a. true;
b. false.

1409. (p. 539) (MD) The difference between staff and line activities in industry is that the line activities are mainly those of auxiliary and advisory services.
a. true;
*b. false.

1410. (pp. 541-542) (MD) In recent years, the proportion of the labor force which belongs to labor unions has not increased; if anything, it has perhaps decreased.
*a. true;
b. false.

1411. (p. 542) (LD) Studies of the way in which labor unions are governed show that they operate pretty much like other bureaucratic organizations.
*a. true;
b. false.

1412. (pp. 545-546) (MD) Experience has shown that the "human relations" approach to employee-management relations which developed from early sociological research has generally gone over well with the workers and increased the prestige and influence of management.
a. true;
*b. false.

1413. (p. 546) (MD) Prior to the Industrial Revolution, there was no recognition of the problem of unemployment.
*a. true;
b. false.

1414. (p. 548) (LD) Most occupational mobility that people experience during their careers is of the vertical kind.
a. true;
*b. false.

1415. (p. 549) (LD) Research on workers' occupational aspirations indicates that younger workers have lower aspirations than older workers.
a. true;
*b. false.

1416. (p. 551) (MD) The occupational roles of men and women appear to be moving in the direction of increasing similarity.
*a. true;
b. false.

1417. (p. 553) (LD) Dissatisfaction and alienation are not automatic by-products of an industrial economy.

*a. true;
 b. false.

1418. (p. 547) (MD) According to Tools of Sociology, "Measuring the
       Labor Force," a person who has never worked is not considered
       unemployed by the Bureau of Labor Statistics.
       *a. true;
        b. false.

1419. (pp. 551-552) (LD) Marx is noted for developing the concept of
       alienation and empirically validating it.
        a. true;
       *b. false.

1420. (p. 552) (MD) Blauner's research on worker alienation supports the
       contention that alienation is widespread among blue-collar workers.
        a. true;
       *b. false.

Fill-In

1421. (p. 531) (MD) Investment by private entrepreneurs in _____
       _____ really marked the beginning of modern capitalism.
       fixed capital

1422. (p. 536) (LD) Profit is the _____ _____ that
       accrues to a product after all the costs have been accounted for.
       surplus value

1423. (p. 538) (LD) In formal bureaucratic structures it is the activity
       of the _____ _____ to implement the policy deci-
       sions from above.
       middle management

1424. (pp. 541-542) (MD) Today, organized labor is predominantly a
       _____ _____ movement.
       working class

1425. (p. 544) (MD) Elton Mayo's research at Western Electric illustrated
       the importance of the primary group and initiated the tradition of
       _____ _____.
       human relations

1426. (pp. 553-555) (LD) Researchers have demonstrated that _____
       increases as rewards decrease.
       alienation

Matching

1427. (pp. 529-532) (MD)
       guild system   depended on the freedom of
                                                 townspeople

"putting-out" system   mainstay of the seventeenth-century English woolen industry

fixed capital   retains the same form over a long period

English Enclosure Acts   created a large labor force

shop production   imposed more control over labor

1428.   (pp. 538-541) (LD)

top managers   coordinating activities for a particular division

line supervision   largest managerial group

line-staff conflicts   focused at positions of vice-presidents

middle management   implement policy

top managerial conflicts   competitive struggle for power

1429.   (pp. 541-544) (LD)

failure of labor movement to grow faster   change from blue-collar to white-collar labor force

project at Western Electric   importance of primary group

unions as economic organizations   run for the benefit of the members

organized labor   predominantly working class

administration of union policy   members elected to committees

1430.   (pp. 546-558) (MD)

alienation   reduced by increasing rewards

occupation   did not exist before the rise of industrial society

unemployment   disproportionately high for young nonwhites

out of the labor force   Current Population Survey

workers as mechanical links   meaninglessness

Short Essay

1431.   (pp. 530-532) (MD)   Briefly describe the factory system.

Major points: investment capital, technology, labor market, shop production.

1432.   (pp. 538-540) (LD)   Name and discuss activities of the major roles in formal bureaucratic structures.

Major points: chief executive--policy making; top managers--responsibility for planning and coordinating activities for the division; middle management--implement policy; line supervision--carry out orders from middle management.

1433.   (pp. 544-546) (LD)   Briefly describe the research project done at Western Electric by Elton Mayo. Was it a "success" or "failure" according to sociologists?

Major points: Mayo demonstrated the importance of the primary group in an impersonal bureaucratic structure; a success.

1434. (pp. 547-556) (MD) Describe briefly Blauner's research on workers and his dimensions of alienation.

Major points: comparative, survey analysis of industrial workers showed that not all blue-collar workers are alienated; dimensions of alienation are powerlessness, meaninglessness, social alienation, and self-estrangement.

Broad Essay

1435. (pp. 528-535) (MD) Trace the development of modern industrialism, clearly explaining the major factors that contributed to its development.

Major points: discussed in text from page 528 through page 535.

1436. (pp. 538-540) (LD) Compare and contrast formal and informal bureaucratic structures. What types of conflict do those in managerial roles often face?

Major points: formal structure: chief executive, top managers, middle management, first-line supervisors; informal structure: power struggles between top managers, antagonisms between line and staff divisions, between top management and middle management, foreman's dilemma.

1437. (pp. 546-558) (MD) Discuss some of the major issues concerning the condition of modern industrial workers.

Major points: alienation, occupational choice and mobility, unemployment.

1438. (pp. 542-544) (LD) Compare the structure of labor organizations with other industrial bureaucracies, making sure to note major similarities and differences.

Major points: unions are run for benefit of members; formal structure similar to bureaucracy, policy handled by committees, importance of secretary-treasurer and stewards.

CHAPTER 19. Education and Social Welfare

Multiple Choice

1439. (p. 560) (LD) The public education and social welfare systems are techniques of social intervention that share the goals of:
a. assimilation and cultural homogeneity;
*b. progress and social justice;
c. differentiation and uniformity;
d. stratification and differentiation;
e. amelioration and "reform."

1440. (p. 561) (LD) In very recent years, the percentage of our total
population that has been formally enrolled in schools has been:
a. about 33 percent;
b. about 50 percent;
c. about 5 percent;
d. about 10 percent;
*e. about 90 percent.

1441. (pp. 562-566) (LD) All of the following were goals of American
education except:
a. social equality;
b. training elites;
c. promoting integration;
*d. cultural pluralism;
e. preventing integration.

1442. (p. 562) (LD) Free public education was delayed in the United
States principally because of:
a. lack of sufficient funds;
b. no support from government officials;
*c. resistance of the property-owning class;
d. shortage of teachers;
e. not having enough books.

1443. (p. 562) (LD) The actual establishment of "free" public education
in "common schools" funded by the state began to be a reality in
American society during which of the following decades?
a. 1780-1789;
*b. 1830-1839;
c. 1870-1879;
d. 1850-1859;
e. 1800-1809.

1444. (p. 562) (MD) The individual who gave American public education many
of its present characteristics (professional training of teachers,
schooling by grades, compulsory attendance, etc.) was the first
secretary of the Massachusetts state board of education:
*a. Horace Mann;
b. John Dewey;
c. Henry Clay;
d. John Gardner;
e. Alfred Landon.

1445. (p. 563) (LD) The concept of racially integrated schools was first
implemented on a serious basis in the South (of the U.S.):
a. during the colonial period (prior to 1780);
b. just prior to the first World War (about 1910);
c. just before the Civil War;
*d. during the decade of "Reconstruction";
e. between 1950 and 1960.

1446. (p. 563) (MD) The Supreme Court's historic decision of 1896
(Plessy vs. Ferguson) established the principle that:
a. schools had to be established in every state;
*b. "separate but equal" educational facilities in the South were
constitutional;

    c. land had to be set aside in each new town for educational
        purposes;
    d. every child had to attend school until a specified age;
    e. religious groups could establish their own schools.

1447. (p. 563) (MD) With the enactment of compulsory schooling laws,
       children of all ethnic backgrounds had to attend. By about 1900,
       one of the principal tasks with which schools were charged was:
       a. preparing the ordinary child for later college work;
       b. maintaining the cultural traditions and language of immigrant
           groups;
       c. leading in the movement toward racial integration by mixing
           children in classes;
      *d. the "Americanization" of children of immigrants;
       e. all of the above.

1448. (p. 564) (MD) Dewey's philosophy of education placed emphasis upon
       the child's learning cooperation and democratic values. The task
       of schooling, he said, should be equivalent to:
       a. education;
       b. training;
       c. learning;
       d. understanding;
      *e. socialization.

1449. (p. 564) (LD) The most influential educator in American society at
       the turn of the century was clearly:
       a. Paul Goodman;
      *b. John Dewey;
       c. Albion Small;
       d. Charles Elwood;
       e. Elmer Dowd.

1450. (p. 564) (LD) Compulsory education brought the entire spectrum of
       American society into schools. While the old goals of Americaniza-
       tion and equalization were still honored in the twentieth century,
       one of the major goals of public education in the U.S. has become:
      *a. vocational sorting;
       b. appreciation of the arts;
       c. training in self-expression;
       d. driver training;
       e. physical education and sports.

1451. (pp. 564-566) (LD) Which of the following strategies are used to
       equalize educational opportunities for minorities?
       a. compensatory education;
       b. transporting minority students to other schools;
       c. aid to minority schools;
      *d. a, b, and c;
       e. b and c only.

1452. (p. 566) (MD) Among the following, which description most adequately
       characterizes the American public's view of the purpose of its
       schools?
      *a. various segments of the public (parents, teachers, administrators,
           and citizen's groups) hold conflicting views concerning what

        schools should do;

b. students are united against teachers in wanting schools to change—they uniformly want more relevant education, while teachers preserve the status quo;

c. the major distinction in goals or purposes is between parents and school authorities (the former are strongly and uniformly dedicated to change);

d. parents tend to insist that schools relax discipline, reduce homework, and bring in more socially relevant topics—students resist these trends;

e. the American public agrees much more than it disagrees concerning the proper goals of public education.

1453. (p. 568) (MD) Education and social stratification are closely related. In fact, it can be said that:
   a. position in the class structure helps determine what education a person gets;
   b. the education people get helps determine their future position in the class structure;
   c. social stratification would be impossible without formal schools;
   d. all of the above are true;
   *e. only a and b are true.

1454. (p. 569) (MD) According to statistics presented in the textbook, a man who has not finished elementary school can expect an income of about what fraction of the income of a college graduate of the same age?
   a. four fifths;
   b. three fourths;
   c. two thirds;
   d. one half;
   *e. less than one half.

1455. (p. 569) (LD) The characteristic of a given person's background that is most clearly predictive of the amount of income he or she will eventually earn as a worker is:
   a. the degree to which he or she has been involved in character-building sports;
   b. whether or not the person comes from a farm background;
   *c. the number of years of education completed;
   d. measured IQ;
   e. the characteristics of the home—for example, persons from broken homes make poor workers.

1456. (pp. 572-573) (LD) An individual's place of residence has a definite effect on the kind of education he or she receives because:
   a. state expenditures per pupil vary greatly;
   b. school districts vary considerably in the quality of education they provide;
   c. family income level in given areas has a considerable relationship to the quality of schools in those areas;
   *d. all of the above are true;
   e. only a and b above are true.

1457. (pp. 572-573) (MD) The chances of a high quality education for poor children in the U.S. are limited because:
   a. teachers are middle class;
   b. health problems are more prevalent among the poor;
   c. educational facilities in poorer districts are of lower quality;
   d. the natural learning ability of poorer children is somewhat lower than that of children from the middle class and above;
   *e. only a, b, and c above.

1458. (pp. 572-573) (MD) A large study of school financing (by Sexton) reported in the text showed which of the following to be true?
   a. the higher the average family income in a school district, the better the education;
   b. the lower the average family income in an area, the poorer the quality of teachers;
   c. federal aid has dramatically changed the relationship between average income and educational quality;
   d. all of the above;
   *e. only a and b.

1459. (pp. 572-573) (LD) When children who live in slums attend school under the supervision of middle-class teachers, they often encounter problems because:
   *a. teachers often expect very little from children who live in slums;
   b. children of slums speak the language with a distinct lack of grammar, syntax, and vocabulary;
   c. children of slums score low on IQ tests, indicating that they lack native learning capacity;
   d. children living in slums have no culture;
   e. all of the above.

1460. (pp. 572-573) (LD) Differences in values between middle-class teachers and pupils from slum areas can cause problems in relating one to the other. For example, compared to children living in slums, teachers are often:
   a. more oriented toward long-range goals;
   b. more motivated toward achievement and upward mobility;
   c. more skilled at planning resources;
   d. more concerned with conventions of manners and dress;
   *e. more likely to value all of the above.

1461. (p. 573) (MD) Research on a high school in a small California town concluded that a particularly important reason why some students were doing poorly in school, or were rebellious, was that:
   a. students were involved in drug abuse and were unable to pursue their studies effectively;
   b. there was too much violence in the school to allow effective study;
   *c. a major gap existed between expectations of the school and the expectations of the students concerning later life;
   d. the school paid inadequate attention to subjects that were necessary to pursue later college studies;
   e. the teachers were poorly trained and not properly prepared for their roles.

1462. (p. 576) (LD) . The large study reported on in the textbook concerning American educational opportunities for the poor was conducted by:
a. Arthur Jensen;
*b. James Coleman;
c. Albert Schanker;
d. Horace Mann;
e. Rosenthal and Jacobson.

1463. (p. 576) (MD) Which of the following was a conclusion of the Coleman report on educational opportunities for the poor in the United States?
a. poor black schools were inferior to poor white schools;
b. both white and black poor are predominantly found in educationally poor schools;
c. on the average, minority students had lower achievement scores than white children in comparable schools;
d. all of the above;
*e. none of the above.

1464. (p. 576) (MD) In advancing the proposition that poorer school performance of blacks was partially due to genetic factors, Arthur Jensen opened the old controversy of:
a. genetic determinism;
b. survival of the fittest;
c. achievement versus ascription;
*d. nature versus nurture;
e. educational determinism.

1465. (p. 577) (LD) Rosenthal and Jacobson argue that minority children do not perform well in school because their teachers do not expect them to do well. This is called:
a. the expectation hypothesis;
*b. a self-fulfilling prophecy;
c. the relative deprivation hypothesis;
d. the discrimination hypothesis;
e. genetic determinism.

1466. (p. 577) (MD) Rosenthal has hypothesized that the self-fulfilling prophecy of school performance is produced by all of the following except:
a. teachers' mood toward students;
b. the extent of feedback given to students;
*c. the fact that "better" students are given more help on exams;
d. the fact that some students are provided with more supplementary materials;
e. the existence of different opportunities for student response.

1467. (p. 578) (LD) The view that poverty is a consequence of the individual's own making is consistent with the orientations of:
a. the culture of poverty thesis;
b. the Protestant Ethic;
c. the social welfare system;
d. Social Darwinism;
*e. b and d only.

1468. (p. 579) (LD) The English Poor Law of the seventeenth century established which of the following principles?
    a. the able-bodied idlers should be punished for their sinfulness;
    b. the poor were given back their small parcels of land taken by the nobility;
    c. the poor could not overthrow the state under penalty of law;
    d. relief for the poor was a collective responsibility;
 *e. relief for the poor was a state responsibility.

1469. (p. 579) (MD) When the Poor Law in England proved to be of limited success, which of the following tactics was chosen to resolve the problems of poverty?
 *a. the poor were exported to the colonies;
    b. the poor were given back their land;
    c. the poor were put in prisons and punished;
    d. the poor were given income subsidies;
    e. nothing further was done to help the poor.

1470. (p. 580) (MD) Social Darwinism found acceptance in nineteenth-century America due to the spirit of:
    a. patriotism;
    b. antiwelfarism;
 *c. rugged individualism;
    d. democracy;
    e. humanitarianism.

1471. (p. 581) (MD) The national government's policy of leaving charity in private hands and local authorities continued until the:
 *a. 1930s;
    b. 1940s;
    c. 1950s;
    d. 1920s;
    e. 1910s.

1472. (p. 582) (LD) Franklin Roosevelt's program of government spending to subsidize economic activity was called:
    a. rugged individualism;
 *b. the New Deal;
    c. the Fair Deal;
    d. Social Darwinism;
    e. the Great Society.

1473. (pp. 582-583) (MD) The Social Security Act of 1935 included provisions for which of the following groups of people?
    a. the aged;
    b. all the unemployed;
    c. dependent children;
    d. all of the above;
 *e. only a and c.

1474. (p. 586) (MD) Several surveys taken in the United States indicate that a majority of Americans believe in which of the following principles regarding poverty.
    a. poverty is socially caused;   d. social welfarism;
    b. poverty is culturally caused; *e. social Darwinism.
    c. poverty is "God work";

1475. (p. 570) (LD) A coefficient or index which summarizes in a single value some quality, trend, or property of an array of measures is called:
*a. a statistic;
 b. a scale;
 c. a datum;
 d. a formula;
 e. a symbol.

1476. (p. 570) (MD) From the discussion of statistical analysis (Tools of Sociology), it is apparent that the mean, the mode, and the median are all measures of which of the following?
 a. variability or dispersion;
*b. central tendency;
 c. standard deviation;
 d. correlation;
 e. path analysis.

True-False

1477. (p. 560) (MD) Industrialization has been the major factor in generating requirements for formal schooling.
*a. true;
 b. false.

1478. (p. 562) (LD) Study after study of the American schools has shown that they have failed to "equalize"; they have merely sorted and selected students for different careers and different ways of life.
*a. true;
 b. false.

1479. (p. 562) (LD) Unlike many European countries, the United States has never regarded its educational institutions primarily as training places for the political elite.
 a. true;
*b. false.

1480. (p. 566) (MD) From the examples given in the textbook, we can conclude that by and large the federal programs set up to improve the educational opportunity and performance of disadvantaged children have been quite successful.
 a. true;
*b. false.

1481. (p. 569) (MD) Average income for people in the U.S. does not necessarily increase with each additional year of education, but rather with each additional level (e.g., high school, college, etc.).
*a. true;
 b. false.

1482. (p. 569) (LD) The number of years of education a person has completed is the best single predictor of his or her economic accomplishments.
*a. true;
 b. false.

1483. (p. 572) (MD) In the United States, income more than any other
single factor has been a limiting influence on a person's chances
for education.
*a. true;
b. false.

1484. (p. 572) (MD) Generally speaking, IQ scores are lower for children
of lower classes than for those of the middle and upper classes.
*a. true;
b. false.

1485. (p. 573) (LD) Evidence about the treatment of lower-class children
by middle-class teachers indicates that lower-class children receive
the necessary approval for what they do if they do it correctly.
a. true;
*b. false.

1486. (p. 573) (LD) In middle-class schools, according to the textbook,
lower-class children are judged mainly for what they are rather than
for what they do.
*a. true;
b. false.

1487. (p. 574) (LD) Equality in educational opportunities for all
Americans has not been realized because federal support for education has been declining.
a. true;
*b. false.

1488. (p. 576) (LD) A conclusion of the Coleman study was that the
quality of the school does not account for the lower scholastic performance of minority students.
*a. true;
b. false.

1489. (p. 576) (LD) Social scientists generally agree with Jensen that
genetic factors result in differences between blacks and whites in
scholastic performance.
a. true;
*b. false.

1490. (p. 577) (MD) Unlike the educational system, the American social
welfare system is not intended to be universal in coverage.
*a. true;
b. false.

1491. (pp. 577-578) (MD) The proportion of a country's population that
is poor and destitute always _decreases_ as the economy of the country
becomes more prosperous.
a. true;
*b. false.

1492. (p. 578) (MD) The English Poor Law was a breakthrough in welfare
systems because it was so successful in solving the problems of
poverty.

a. true;
*b. false.

1493. (p. 580) (LD) Social Darwinism and rugged individualism were the motive forces behind the creation of a national system of social welfare in the United States.
a. true;
*b. false.

1494. (p. 582) (MD) The Social Security Act of 1935 remains America's basic form of relief for the poor.
*a. true;
b. false.

1495. (p. 584) (LD) No significant changes have taken place in the overall approach to social welfare in the United States since 1930.
a. true;
*b. false.

Fill-In

1496. (p. 562) (LD) The goal of education under colonial rule was primarily that of _____ _____.

training elites

1497. (p. 569) (MD) The single best predictor of an individual's economic performance in the labor force is _____.

education

1498. (p. 572) (LD) The _____ the socioeconomic level of one's family, the higher the probability that education will be terminated early.

lower

1499. (p. 580) (LD) The spirit of rugged individualism in America led to the acceptance of the ideology of _____ _____.

Social Darwinism

1500. (p. 582) (MD) Franklin D. Roosevelt's program of government subsidies for economic activity was called the _____
_____.

New Deal

1501. (p. 570) (MD) The _____ _____ is an index of scatter used to indicate the degree of variability in an array of measures.

standard deviation

Matching

1502. (pp. 562-566) (MD)

spread of equality	resisted by property-owning class
compulsory education law of 1874	eliminated cheap labor pool
teachers made into primary agents of socialization	John Dewey
education in late eighteenth century in the U.S.	training elites
supported by federal funds	education in 1960s

1503. (pp. 568-573) (LD)

the diploma	commercial value
quality of school	not related to performance
parents' income	positively related to quality of education
personal values	social class differences
performance of lower-class children	assessed by middle-class values

1504. (pp. 569-573) (MD)

best predictor of economic performance	number of years of education completed
most important factor in determining quality of education	parents' income
influence of family background on educational achievement	father's socioeconomic level
low IQ scores for lower-class children	low verbal skills
inconsistent student expectations	rebellious behavior

1505. (pp. 580-584) (LD)

rugged individualism	Social Darwinism
government subsidized economy	the New Deal
relief for poor	Social Security Act of 1935
low-income housing	the Fair Deal
medical care for aged	the Great Society

Short Essay

1506. (pp. 568-573) (MD) Discuss several social variables related to education.

Major points: position in the social structure helps determine educational attainment, and education helps determine future position in the social structure; education is positively related to income, place of residence, family income, peer group influences, and race.

1507. (pp. 572-573) (MD) Discuss the arguments given for the theory that there is "value-influence" in the teaching role.

Major points: social class differences in personal values; teachers drawn from middle class and hold its orientation; teachers use middle-class values in assessing the merits of middle- and lower-class students; self-fulfilling prophecy.

1508. (pp. 574-577) (LD) Discuss three attempts to explain the causes of differences in scholastic performance.

Major points: compensatory education (Coleman's study), the genetic influence hypothesis (Jensen), and the self-fulfilling prophecy hypothesis (Rosenthal and Jacobson).

1509. (pp. 584-587) (LD) Discuss the outlooks for further change in the American welfare system.

Major points: American attitudes toward social welfare are products of earlier societal conditions but changes are taking place; welfare expenditures have increased, and experiments are being undertaken to judge the effects of different welfare systems.

Broad Essay

1510. (pp. 562-566) (MD) Changing social conditions in our country caused many changes in the educational system beginning in the seventeenth century. Pick at least four goals of American education and trace their evolution.

Major points: training elites, spreading equality, promoting and preventing integration, Americanizing immigrants, preparing future citizens, vocational sorting, educating the expert society.

1511. (pp. 568-573) (MD) Discuss at length the factors that affect the quality and quantity of education in our society today.

Major points: place of residence and income, family background, teachers' expectations and values, race.

1512. (pp. 577-581) (LD) Discuss the origins of American orientations toward welfare.

Major points: English Poor Law of early 1600s established alms-houses, work, apprenticeships, and money for poor; poor were exported to colonies; rugged individualism retarded welfare programs until social responsibility was recognized and finally implemented in the 1930s.

1513. (pp. 582-584) (LD) Briefly discuss the major pieces of legislation which established a national welfare system in the United States.

Major points: the New Deal of Roosevelt, the Social Security Act of 1935, Truman's Fair Deal, Eisenhower's National Defense Act, Kennedy's War on Poverty, and Johnson's Great Society.

CHAPTER 20. The Sociologist in Contemporary Society

Multiple Choice

1514. (p. 592) (MD) One of the most significant areas of research for the future development of sociology is:

a. unraveling the causes of crime;
b. studying the rising trends in student militancy;
c. aiding the police in controlling unruly minorities;
d. studying the impact of "hippy" communes;
*e. evaluation of social programs.

1515. (pp. 592-594) (LD) The involvement of sociologists in national policy planning in the future will probably involve which of the following?
a. devising "social indicators";
b. serving as consultants for political leaders;
c. serving on a national council of social advisors;
d. forming policy-formulating study groups in professional associations;
*e. all of the above.

1516. (p. 592) (MD) The central role of sociologists in public policy is:
*a. gathering and interpreting facts to ascertain causes of social conditions;
b. legislating social programs;
c. seeing that federal money is spent properly;
d. insuring that personal biases are not introduced in social programs;
e. sociologists do not have a role in policy research since they are scientists.

1517. (p. 594) (MD) The textbook proposes that social activism can contribute to progress in social science itself by:
a. calling attention to important areas of research that have been overlooked;
b. challenging sociologists to reorder their research priorities from time to time;
c. challenging sociologists to examine the problem of research support more closely;
*d. all of the above;
e. only a and b.

1518. (pp. 594-596) (MD) Which of the following guidelines of the ASA Code of Ethics arose out of the controversy over Project Camelot?
a. presentation of research findings;
b. distortion of findings by sponsor;
c. acknowledgment of research collaboration and assistance;
d. disassociation from unethical research arrangements;
*e. b and d only.

1519. (p. 595) (LD) Which of the following is the "sociological dilemma" discussed at the end of the text?
a. protest vs. principles;
b. pure vs. applied research;
*c. social action vs. scientific detachment;
d. unobligated vs. financially supported research;
e. all of the above.

1520. (p. 595) (MD) The authors make which of the following points about the sociologist's orientation to work?
a. sociologists who take a detached and objective stance toward

their knowledge are artificially isolating themselves from
their society;
b. sociologists who actively enter a struggle to change society
are in danger of losing their identities as scientists and
becoming partisan;
c. partisans must necessarily select their social innovators on
the basis of personal values or ideology rather than scientific
method;
*d. all of the above;
e. only b and c.

1521. (pp. 597-598) (MD) Which of the following has(have) been solutions
to the "sociologist's dilemma" (social action vs. scientific
detachment)?
a. selection of research problems;
b. activism in teaching;
c. deemphasis of scientific pursuits;
d. social engineering;
*e. all of the above.

1522. (pp. 597-598) (MD) It is important that sociological research be
conducted according to certain principles because:
a. sociology is a science;
*b. sociology can influence human lives;
c. otherwise, sociologists will not be able to change social
conditions;
d. otherwise, sociologists will not be able to get research funds;
e. all of the above.

1523. (p. 598) (MD) The ethics of research were discussed in relation to
Humphreys' research on the "Tearoom Trade." The ethical problems
in this research centered around:
a. subversion;
b. insurgency;
c. participant observation;
*d. deception;
e. clandestine activities.

1524. (p. 599) (LD) The textbook cites some criticisms that have been
leveled at Humphreys' research on the "Tearoom Trade." They include:
a. infringement of privacy;
b. lying about purposes;
c. he may have brought harm to the subjects;
d. he damaged the credibility of other researchers;
*e. all of the above.

1525. (p. 596) (MD) Among the items in the ASA Code of Ethics are all
except which one of the following?
a. objectivity in research;
b. respect for privacy of research subjects;
c. undistorted presentation of research findings;
*d. service to humans;
e. disclosure of financial support.

1526. (p. 596) (LD) A code of ethics covering both the research process
and applications of sociological findings has been adopted and

approved by members of:

*a. the American Sociological Association;

b. the National Federation of Sociology Teachers;

c. the Radical Coalition of Sociologists;

d. the U.S. Bureau of Standards;

e. the American Association of University Professors.

True-False

1527. (p. 590) (LD) The founders of sociology hoped to develop a science of society that would provide a complete guide to the solution of social problems and the achievement of a just and harmonious social order.

*a. true;

b. false.

1528. (p. 591) (MD) The authors of the text contend that, because sociology deals directly with the study of people, it seems to be the only scientific field that has to cope with ethical questions.

a. true;

*b. false.

1529. (p. 592) (LD) The evaluation of government social programs, say the authors of the text, is at present beyond the available tools and capabilities of sociology.

a. true;

*b. false.

1530. (pp. 597-601) (MD) Sociologists are virtually unanimous in their condemnation of Humphreys' research on impersonal sex in public places.

a. true;

*b. false.

1531. (p. 597) (MD) In many ways the current debate over activism vs. scholarship has characterized sociology from its beginning.

*a. true;

b. false.

1532. (p. 597) (MD) According to the authors of the text, activism among sociologists has actually been with us quite a long time.

*a. true;

b. false.

1533. (p. 597) (LD) According to the authors of the textbook, the majority of articles published in professional sociological journals are abstract and not concerned with specific societal problems.

a. true;

*b. false.

1534. (p. 597) (LD) The authors of the textbook argue that social activism can take place in the classroom.

*a. true;

b. false.

1535. (p. 598) (LD) Humphreys' research on the "Tearoom Trade" was

criticized because of his carelessness in protecting the anonymity of his subjects from the public.
a. true;
*b. false.

1536. (p. 596) (MD) The Code of Ethics of the American Sociological Association does not have any applicability outside the United States.
a. true;
*b. false.

1537. (p. 596) (LD) According to the Code of Ethics of the American Sociological Association, sociologists need not report fully all sources of financial support for their published research.
a. true;
*b. false.

Fill-In

1538. (p. 593) (LD) Developing _____ _____ is an important area of sociological activity in the investigation of the nation's well-being.

social indicators

1539. (p. 598) (MD) Humphreys' research report on impersonal sex in public places is called _____ _____.

Tearoom Trade

Short Essay

1540. (pp. 591-594) (LD) Briefly explain some of the ways in which sociologists are involved in public policy.

Major points: designing and evaluating social programs, policy research, developing social indicators, sociological advisors, sociological lobbyists.

1541. (pp. 598-601) (MD) Briefly identify and discuss the ethical issues involved in Laud Humphreys' Tearoom Trade.

Major points: the criticisms include Humphreys' deception, his misrepresenting himself to the subjects, his violation of privacy of the subjects, and the possible harm that could have been brought upon the subjects. All of these criticisms have been answered by Humphreys' advisors, but Humphreys himself does not believe that he would follow the same practices.

Broad Essay

1542. (pp. 594-596) (LD) One of the controversial issues in modern sociology has been the ethical responsibilities of the sociologist. Outline what you take those responsibilities to be, and present such arguments as you can for your point of view.

Major points: responsibilities are listed in the ASA Code of Ethics on page 596.

1543. (pp. 595-597) (MD) Identify the "sociologist's dilemma" and assess the suggestions for resolving that dilemma.

Major points: ethical neutrality: hard for one to remain objective
and conform to one's ideas of social responsibility; active participation: if one takes an active part in rearranging the social
order, one may lose credibility as a scientist; suggestions: selection of research problems, deemphasize or abandon scientific pursuits, and exercise the role of teacher as activist.